*Introduction
to Logic and Sets*

Introduction to Logic and Sets

Robert R. Christian
The University of British Columbia

GINN-BLAISDELL

A Xerox Company

WALTHAM, MASSACHUSETTS / TORONTO / LONDON

Preface to the Second Edition

The present version of *Introduction to Logic and Sets* retains the organization and most of the details of the original preliminary edition. Broadly, the changes are the following: First, a few topics have been dropped. These consisted of a more detailed treatment of the truth value function, the algebra of conditions, and general unions and intersections. Second, there has been a slight shuffling of topics. This, I believe, has improved the organization of the book without changing it in any essential way. Third, some of the notation and terminology has been changed slightly, but without departing from what is in common use today. Fourth, a few exercises have been dropped, and a few have been added. Fifth, the answers have been reworked, corrected, and moved to the back of the book. Sixth, an index has been prepared.

As in the preliminary edition, sections marked with an asterisk (*) may be omitted entirely without disturbing the continuity. These sections contain topics which are less important than the others.

Finally, I would like to thank the following people, whose criticisms of the preliminary edition have helped me in preparing the present edition: Julia Wells Bower, T. C. Holyoke, R. E. Johnson, John G. Kemeny, William G. Lister, Bruce E. Meserve, Ernest C. Schlesinger, Hugh A. Thurston, Charles T. Wolf.

ROBERT R. CHRISTIAN

Vancouver, B.C., Canada
May, 1964

Preface to the First Edition

This book is an introduction to some of the basic ideas, terminology, and notation of logic and sets. Most of the material is important because it is basic to mathematics as it is known today.

The subject matter has appeared elsewhere, but not in the present form. Various portions can be found in more formal works in logic, sets, and electrical engineering. Much of the material can also be found in certain elementary texts intended for use in "modern" programs in mathematics, both in high school and in college. The treatment is, I believe, more leisurely, yet more systematic, than that found in most of these elementary texts.

Introduction to Logic and Sets was written as a supplement for existing mathematics courses, both in high school and in college. Certain portions of algebra, geometry, and trigonometry can be clarified greatly by using the language of logic and sets. Some of these portions are identities and equations in algebra and trigonometry, and locus problems in geometry. Specific indications can be found here and in Robert E. K. Rourke's article "Some implications of twentieth century mathematics for high schools" (*The Mathematics Teacher,* Volume LI, Number 2, February 1958). Again, this book contains all the set-theoretic material needed for modern treatments of elementary probability and statistics.

This treatment makes little contact with the important issues of logic and set theory. The theory of inference is given but passing mention, and mention of cardinal equivalence is omitted altogether. These issues are highly sophisticated, and as a result I do not feel that they are suitable for study in beginning courses in mathematics. I do feel, however, that the *language* of logic and sets must sooner or later play an important part in elementary mathematical instruction. Therefore, the emphasis here is on language and notation, rather than on sophisticated theories.

Most of the material is easy and may be covered rapidly. Sections marked with an asterisk (*) may be omitted entirely without disturbing the continuity.

The exercises are designed to test the student's comprehension of the material, not his mastery of techniques. The text contains very little work with "type" problems: The student is expected to do his own thinking. Most of the exercises are fairly easy, but some are not. Many of the more difficult exercises are marked with the "sharp" sign (♯) of music.

I would like to thank Rodrigo Restrepo, who took an early interest in the manuscript and followed it through several drafts with frank, constructive, and good-natured criticism; Ralph James, who made many cogent remarks on the first draft and agreed to its use in experimental sections at the University of British Columbia; Mrs. Catherine Easto, who helped with the typing; Roger Purves, who made numerous useful suggestions; and, finally, the many students whose anonymous comments led to significant improvements in the manuscript.

ROBERT R. CHRISTIAN

Vancouver, B.C., Canada
July, 1958

Contents

Part I

Logic

1. Introduction

The title of this part is a misnomer. *Webster's New Collegiate Dictionary* of 1953 defines logic as "the science that deals with the canons and criteria of thought and demonstration; the science of the formal principles of reasoning." Logic is a complicated subject, and it would be presumptuous to suppose that we could deal with it in a small compass. The chief aim of Part I is much more modest. It is merely to expose, clearly and carefully, the meanings of a few words and symbols used in present-day logic and mathematics.

Actually, there is more to Part I than just a few definitions. There is also an attempt to show, by force of example, that careful formulation of the meanings of words and symbols can have fruitful consequences. Hence the applications to black boxes and switching networks found in the last three sections. These applications are part of neither logic nor mathematics, and will not be referred to in the sequel. Their function here is only to hint at the fertile relationship which exists between mathematics and its applications.

2. The Notion of Equality

In everyday language many words have a number of different meanings and are used in a number of different ways. The word "is," for example, is sometimes used in the sense of *identical with,* as in the sentence "Rome is the capital of Italy." Here the word "Rome" refers to the same city as does the phrase "the capital of Italy": Rome *is identical with* the capital of Italy. Again, the word

3

"is" can be used in the sense of belonging to a certain category. The sentence "Socrates is dead," for example, means that Socrates belongs to the category of dead people. It is nonsense to say that Socrates is identical with dead, so the second meaning is certainly different from the first. Still other meanings of the word "is" can be found in a dictionary, under the heading "be."

The ability to use words in different senses makes everyday language far richer than it might otherwise be. But this richness is bought at the price of possible ambiguity. A statement may be perfectly intelligible, yet open to a number of different interpretations. When ambiguity must be avoided at all costs—as in legal documents and scientific discourse—it is necessary to use a language other than that of every day.

To render the first of the above two meanings of the word "is"—that of identity—we have adopted the word "equals," symbolized by the familiar equality sign ($=$). For example, the statement that $2 + 3$ equals $1 + 4$ [in symbols, that $2 + 3 = 1 + 4$], is a statement that $2 + 3$ and $1 + 4$ are one and the same number—namely the number 5. Abstractly, the statement "$x = y$" is a statement that x is the same thing as y, or that "x" and "y" are names for the same thing, whatever that thing might be. The word "equal" will also refer to this relation of identity.

You should be aware that the word "equal" has meanings other than the one just mentioned. For example, a different meaning occurs in the statement "All men are created equal." This statement does not mean that all men are created the same man (absurd thought) but rather that they all have (or should have) the same political rights. Even in mathematics one finds different meanings for the word "equal." Two line segments, *AB* and *CD,* for example, are often said to be "equal" when they have the same length. But for us the statement that *AB* equals *CD* will mean that *AB* and *CD* are one and the same.

The idea of equality used in this book is most frequently applied in a technique called *substitution*. If "x" and "y" stand for the same thing (that is, if $x = y$) then whatever is true of x must also be true of y, and whatever is true of y must also be true of x. If we know, for example, that Rome $=$ the capital of Italy and that St.

Peter's is in Rome, then we can conclude that St. Peter's is in the capital of Italy. Again, if $x = a + b$ and $x^3 - 3x^2 + 3x - 1 = 0$ then we can conclude that $(a + b)^3 - 3(a + b)^2 + 3(a + b) - 1 = 0$ also.

Two properties of equality deserve special mention. One is the property of *transitivity:* If $a = b$ and $b = c$ then $a = c$. This property has frequent use in mathematics. The other is that of *symmetry: If $a = b$ then $b = a$. An equality can be read in either direction.* Some students are greatly confused when this property is applied. For example, some students of elementary algebra can easily see why $a(b + c) = ab + ac$, but have great trouble in seeing why $ab + ac = a(b + c)$. They would not have so much trouble, of course, if they fully understood that equality is symmetric.

It is usual in mathematics to negate a symbol by means of a stroke. Thus the symbol "$\neq$" (equality sign with stroke) means "is not equal to" or "is not identical with." If "x" and "y" stand for *different* things then x is not equal to y and we write "$x \neq y$."

EXERCISES

1. In some of the following sentences the word "is" can meaningfully be replaced by the equality sign ($=$). State which.

    (a) A little learning is a dangerous thing.
    (b) A little learning is not a dangerous thing.
    (c) Imitation is the sincerest form of flattery.
    (d) Imitation is not the sincerest form of flattery.
    (e) The greatest of these is charity.
    (f) The greatest of these is not charity.
    (g) The female of the species is more deadly than the male.
    (h) The female of the species is not more deadly than the male.
    (i) It is easier to catch flies with honey than with vinegar.
    (j) It is not easier to catch flies with honey than with vinegar.
    (k) Silence is the most perfect expression of scorn.
    (l) Silence is not the most perfect expression of scorn.
    (m) The game is up.

2. In some of the sentences of the preceding exercise the phrase "is not" can meaningfully be replaced by the inequality sign ($\neq$). State which.

3. Propositions and Truth Values

Logic is a study which is of value in a great number of fields. It is especially important in mathematics, but there is hardly a field—psychology, economics, football, physics, language—which does not use logic. One of the reasons for the wide applicability of logic is its great generality. Its subject matter embraces features common to practically all fields. Specifically, practically all fields make use of statements which are considered to be true or false, but, of course, not both true and false. Statements of this sort are called *propositions,* and form the basic raw material of logic. We shall start by considering the relation between a proposition and its truth or falsity.

We shall say that a proposition has the *truth value T* if it is true and *truth value F* if it is false. [Read "*T*" as "tee," not as "true."] For example, the statement "Rome is the capital of Italy" is a true proposition, so its truth value is *T*. Again, "Canada is part of the United States" is a proposition whose truth value is *F*.

In mathematics and logic it is convenient to introduce abbreviations. When we expect to talk about something quite a lot we introduce a short name for this thing. You should be familiar with this process from your study of algebra, where you used letters to stand for numbers. ["Let q be the number of quarters in Jim's pocket. Then . . . ."] In logic it is customary to let letters stand for whole propositions. For example, in some discussions we might use the letter "r" to stand for the entire proposition "Rome is the capital of Italy." In other discussions, of course, we might want to let "r" stand for something else.

In this chapter we shall use a certain shorthand notation to refer to the truth values of propositions. We shall denote the truth value of a proposition by writing the Greek letter "τ" (tau), followed by the name of the proposition in parentheses, as in the example

$$\tau(\text{"Rome is the capital of Italy"}).$$

[Read this as "the truth value of 'Rome is the capital of Italy,'"
or as "tau of 'Rome is the capital of Italy'."] Using the equality
sign in the sense of the preceding section (and "*r*" as in the preceding paragraph) we write "$\tau(r) = T$" to indicate that the given proposition is true.

Example A. Let "*c*" stand for "Canada is part of the United
States." What is $\tau(c)$?

Solution. The given proposition is false, so $\tau(c) = F$.

The exercises which follow are only for practice in using the
above ideas. They are not important in themselves, except to let
you know how much of the above you understand.

EXERCISES

1. Find $\tau(p)$ if $p = $ "Paris is the capital of France."
2. Find $\tau(\text{"}3 \times 7 + 8 \times 8 = 7 \times 9 + 4 \times 5\text{"})$.
3. (a) Find a number which, when placed in the boxes below,
      turns the given "open" equation into a true proposition:

   $$7 \;=\; 2 \times \boxed{} \;+\; 3 \times \boxed{} \;-\; 13.$$

   (b) Find a number which, when placed in the boxes, turns
      the given "open" equation into a false proposition. Can
      you find three such numbers?
4. If we let "*x*" stand for the number 13, find $\tau(\text{"}7x + 5 = 98\text{"})$.

4. *Basic Operations*

Now that we have introduced the notions of proposition and
truth value, we can go on to show how new propositions may be
constructed from old ones. The principal tools used in this construction are the words ***and, or,*** and ***not.*** In logic these words

are used in very nearly the same way as they are in everyday language, but there are important differences. In particular, usage in logic is determined by strict convention, whereas in everyday language usage is more flexible. Other differences in meaning and use will be apparent as we proceed.

Two propositions may be combined by means of the word **and** to yield another proposition, called the *conjunction* of the two propositions. The conjunction of the proposition "Rome is the capital of Italy" and the proposition "Canada is part of the United States," for example, is the proposition "Rome is the capital of Italy **and** Canada is part of the United States." In logic, the usual convention is to consider the conjunction of two propositions to be true when both propositions are true, and false otherwise. Thus, by convention, the proposition "Rome is the capital of Italy **and** Canada is part of the United States" is false, because the proposition "Canada is part of the United States" is false.

We shall use the symbol "$\wedge$" for the operation of conjunction; the conjunction of two propositions a and b is written as "$a \wedge b$." With abbreviations used in the preceding section, $r \wedge c$ is the proposition "Rome is the capital of Italy **and** Canada is part of the United States." In this case $\tau(r \wedge c) = F$. Similarly, if p is "Paris is the capital of France" then $r \wedge p$ is "Rome is the capital of Italy **and** Paris is the capital of France," and $\tau(r \wedge p) = T$.

Another way to combine two propositions is by means of the word **or**. The result of this combination is called the *disjunction* of the two propositions. The disjunction of the proposition "Rome is the capital of Italy" and the proposition "Canada is part of the United States," for example, is the proposition "Rome is the capital of Italy **or** Canada is part of the United States." In logic, the usual convention is to consider the disjunction of two propositions to be false when both propositions are false and true otherwise. Thus, by convention, the proposition "Rome is the capital of Italy **or** Paris is the capital of France" is true, because the propositions "Rome is the capital of Italy" and "Paris is the capital of France" are not both false. Note that the word **or** is used in only one of the senses of everyday language, and a fairly unusual one at that. We shall encounter a more usual meaning later, in an exercise.

We shall use the symbol "$\vee$" for the operation of disjunction; the disjunction of two propositions a and b is written as "$a \vee b$." With the above abbreviations $r \vee c$ is "Rome is the capital of Italy **or** Canada is part of the United States," and $\tau(r \vee c) = T$.

The last operation considered in this section is the operation of *negation*. The negation of a proposition is the expression **It is false that** followed by the proposition itself. The negation of "Rome is the capital of Italy" is "**It is false that** Rome is the capital of Italy." By convention, the negation of a proposition is considered false when the proposition is true, and true when the proposition is false.

We shall use the symbol "$\sim$" (read as "**not**") for the operation of negation; the negation of a proposition a is written as "$\sim a$." With the above abbreviations $\sim r$ ("**not** r") is "**It is false that** Rome is the capital of Italy," and $\tau(\sim r) = F$. Similarly, $\tau(\sim c) = T$.

Do not be upset by some bizarre propositions which can result from the use of the logical operations. For example, "Rome is the capital of Italy **or** $1 + 1 = 5$" sounds strange, but it is a true proposition. Such propositions are harmless and normally do not occur in mathematics.

Sometimes more than one logical operation occurs in a proposition, as in the examples which follow. These examples use the abbreviations mentioned above.

Example A. Use the above abbreviations and translate the proposition "Rome is the capital of Italy and it is false that Canada is part of the United States" into symbols. What is the truth value of this proposition?

Solution. With parentheses used for grouping (in much the same way as in high-school algebra), the given proposition is $r \wedge (\sim c)$. Since $\tau(r) = T$ and $\tau(\sim c) = T$, we must have $\tau(r \wedge (\sim c)) = T$.

To reduce the number of parentheses needed for grouping, we usually omit parentheses around negations of propositions. For example, instead of writing "$r \wedge (\sim c)$" we write "$r \wedge \sim c$." In order to keep this convention unambiguous, we agree that any "$\sim$"

is to apply only to the first proposition immediately to the right of this symbol. For example, if a and b are propositions, then $\sim a \vee b$ is $(\sim a) \vee b$, not $\sim (a \vee b)$. The "$\sim$" goes with "a," not with "$a \vee b$."

Example B. Translate the proposition "Paris is the capital of France **and,** moreover, Canada is part of the United States **or** Rome is the capital of Italy" into symbols. [Let $p =$ "Paris is the capital of France."] What is the truth value of this proposition?

Solution. With parentheses used for grouping, the given proposition is $p \wedge (c \vee r)$. Clearly, $\tau(c \vee r) = T$, because $\tau(r) = T$. Since $\tau(p) = T$, it follows that $\tau(p \wedge (c \vee r)) = T$ also.

In Example B, note that some sort of system of grouping is needed to avoid ambiguity. This is true for the verbal statement under consideration as well as its symbolic representation. In the verbal statement the word "moreover" fulfills the same function as parentheses in setting off the clause "Canada is part of the United States **or** Rome is the capital of Italy" from the rest of the sentence.

When a proposition has been translated into symbols as in the above examples it is said to be *in symbolic form*. In translating propositions into symbolic form any letter may be used to designate any proposition. But *the same letter must never be used to designate two different propositions in the same discussion.* If "d" were used for both "Dermatology fascinates Tom" and "Dancing girls fascinate John," for example, then "$d \wedge \sim d$" would be hopelessly ambiguous. From this example it should be clear that the above rule must always be observed to avoid confusion. With appropriate modification the rule applies to all other parts of mathematics.

The symbols $\wedge$, $\vee$, and $\sim$ will always stand for the operations **and,** **or,** and **not,** respectively. It is these symbols, rather than the particular letters used for propositions, that are most important in determining symbolic form. To illustrate, "Rome is the capital of Italy **and** Paris is the capital of France" can be abbreviated to "$i \wedge f$" as well as to "$r \wedge p$." The letters are different but the essential *form* is not. Similarly, the form $r \vee p$ is essentially the same as the form $c \lor u$. Again, the form $(p \land c) \lor (p \land r)$ is essentially the same as the form $(r \land u) \lor (r \land c)$. In the sections which follow we shall see that the study of forms is mathematically more important than the study of propositions.

EXERCISES

1. Let y be "The night is young" and let b be "You are beautiful." Give the verbal meaning of each of the following as simply as you can:

   (a) $\sim b$.
   (b) $y \lor b$.
   (c) $\sim y \lor b$.
   (d) $y \lor \sim b$.
   (e) $\sim y \land \sim b$.
   (f) $\sim \sim y$.
   (g) $(\sim y \land b) \lor (y \land \sim b)$.

2. Let w be "Willie is silly," let j be "Jane is plain," and let a be "Art is smart." Write each of the following propositions in symbolic form:

   (a) It is false that Willie is silly (Willie is not silly).
   (b) Willie is silly or Jane is plain.
   (c) Jane is not plain or Art is smart.
   (d) Willie is not silly and Jane is not plain.
   (e) It is false that (Willie is silly and Art is smart).
   (f) (Willie is silly and Art is smart) or Jane is plain.
   (g) Willie is silly and (Art is smart or Jane is plain).
   (h) It is false that Art is not smart.
   (i) Willie is not silly or Art is not smart.

3. Let p be "$1 + 1 = 2$" and let q be "$2 + 1 = 8$." Determine the truth value of each of the following:

   (a) $p \land \sim q$.
   (b) $p \lor \sim q$.
   (c) $\sim p \land q$.
   (d) $\sim p \lor q$.
   (e) $\sim p \land \sim q$.
   (f) $\sim p \lor \sim q$.
   (g) $\sim(\sim p \land \sim q)$.
   (h) $p \land (\sim p \lor q)$.
   (i) $(\sim p \land q) \lor (p \land \sim q)$.

5. Truth Tables

The most striking feature of the operations **and, or,** and **not,** as used in logic, is their complete lack of ambiguity. Given the truth values of the components of a compound proposition, one can always determine whether this proposition is true or false. For example (and here we use abbreviations from the preceding section) the proposition $p \wedge \sim c$ is true because p is true and $\sim c$ is true. Our task in this section is to examine a device, called a *truth table,* which yields all possible truth values of a compound logical form, given the possible truth values of its components.

Suppose we are given two propositions, p and q. Then perhaps both of these propositions are true. On the other hand, p may be true and q false, or q true and p false. It might even happen that both propositions are false. If both p and q are true, then $p \wedge q$ is true; in all other cases $p \wedge q$ is false. This information is summarized in Figure 5.1, which is a truth table for the operation of

$\tau(p)$	$\tau(q)$	$\tau(p \wedge q)$
T	T	T
T	F	F
F	T	F
F	F	F

FIGURE 5.1

conjunction. Note that there are exactly four possibilities, and that each line of the truth table corresponds to one possibility.

In the same way one can form truth tables for the operations of disjunction and negation. These tables are given in Figures 5.2 and 5.3, respectively.

It is not hard to construct truth tables for compound operations such as that given by the form $p \wedge \sim q$. Two rules will be helpful:

12

$\tau(p)$	$\tau(q)$	$\tau(p \vee q)$
T	T	T
T	F	T
F	T	T
F	F	F

FIGURE 5.2

$\tau(p)$	$\tau(\sim p)$
T	F
F	T

FIGURE 5.3

First, observe the usual conventions regarding the grouping of terms by means of parentheses. [Although these conventions have not been explained here, you should have no trouble with them, because they are very much like those of high-school algebra. Think of "∧" and "∨" as two varieties of "+" and group accordingly. The symbol "∼" has already been discussed.] Second, allow enough rows in the table to cover all possible cases. Allow two rows for forms, such as $p \vee \sim \sim p$, that involve only one basic component; four rows for forms, such as $p \wedge \sim q$, that involve two basic components; and eight rows for forms that involve three basic components. Figures 5.4 and 5.5 are truth tables for $p \wedge \sim q$ and $(\sim p \wedge q) \vee (p \wedge \sim q)$, respectively. Since both of these forms involve two basic components, both truth tables have four rows. For brevity the symbol "τ" is omitted from these tables and from all that follow.

p	q	$\sim q$	$p \wedge \sim q$
T	T	F	F
T	F	T	T
F	T	F	F
F	F	T	F

FIGURE 5.4

p	q	$\sim p$	$\sim q$	$\sim p \wedge q$	$p \wedge \sim q$	$(\sim p \wedge q) \vee (p \wedge \sim q)$
T	T	F	F	F	F	F
T	F	F	T	F	T	T
F	T	T	F	T	F	T
F	F	T	T	F	F	F

FIGURE 5.5

If one is lazy but careful one may abbreviate a long truth table as in Figure 5.6. It will be left to you to puzzle out the process

$(\sim$	p	$\wedge$	$q)$	$\vee$	$(p$	$\wedge$	$\sim$	$q)$
F	T	F	T	F	T	F	F	T
F	T	F	F	T	T	T	T	F
T	F	T	T	T	F	F	F	T
T	F	F	F	F	F	F	T	F

FIGURE 5.6

involved in making such an abbreviated table. The final result of the process is given in the column headed "$\vee$."

EXERCISES

1. Construct a truth table for each of the following:

   (a) $\sim \sim p \vee p$.
   (b) $p \wedge p$.
   (c) $p \vee \sim p$.
   (d) $p \wedge \sim p$.
   (e) $p \vee \sim q$.
   (f) $\sim (p \vee q)$.
   (g) $\sim p \wedge \sim q$.
   (h) $\sim p \vee q$.
   (i) $\sim (p \wedge \sim q)$.
   (j) $\sim p \vee \sim q$.
   (k) $(p \vee q) \wedge \sim (p \wedge q)$.
   (l) $(p \wedge \sim q) \vee (\sim p \wedge q)$.

(m) $(p \wedge q) \vee \sim (p \vee q)$.

(n) $\sim [p \wedge (\sim p \vee q)] \vee q$.

(o) $\sim \{\sim [\sim p \vee (p \wedge \sim q)] \wedge \sim q\}$.

(p) $p \vee (q \wedge r)$.

(q) $(p \vee q) \wedge (p \vee r)$.

2. (a) Show that (h) and (i) of Exercise 1 have the same truth value, regardless of the truth values of p and q.

  (b) Do the same for (p) and (q).

  (c) Find other consecutive pairs which always have the same truth value.

3. Show that the propositions "It is false that (Bert is a flirt or Jane is plain)" and "Bert is not a flirt and Jane is not plain" have the same truth value.

4. How many lines should be allowed for a truth table involving four basic components (say p, q, r, and s)? Five basic components? Eight?

5. Construct a truth table for the form $(p \wedge q) \vee (r \wedge s)$.

6. *Equivalent Propositions and Forms*

From the preceding work you may have noticed that in logic we are really more interested in the truth value of a proposition than in its meaning. More abstractly, sometimes our only interest is in whether two given propositions have the same truth value. When two propositions do have the same truth value then they are said to be *equivalent*. We shall write "$p \Leftrightarrow q$" to indicate that propositions p and q are equivalent (have the same truth value) and "$p \nLeftrightarrow q$" to indicate that p and q are not equivalent. Thus

$$p \Leftrightarrow q \text{ if } \tau(p) = \tau(q)$$

and

$$p \nLeftrightarrow q \text{ if } \tau(p) \neq \tau(q)$$

Example A. The propositions "$1 + 1 = 2$" and "$2 + 2 = 4$" are equivalent, because both are true.

Example B. The propositions "$1 + 1 = 5$" and "$2 + 1 = 17$" are equivalent, because both are false.

Example C. The propositions "$1 + 1 = 2$" and "$2 + 1 = 17$" are not equivalent, because

$$T = \tau(\text{``}1 + 1 = 2\text{''}) \neq \tau(\text{``}2 + 1 = 17\text{''}) = F.$$

Example D. If p is *any* proposition—true *or* false—then $\sim \sim p$ and p are equivalent, because $\tau(\sim \sim p) = \tau(p)$, as indicated in Figure 6.1.

p	$\sim p$	$\sim \sim p$
T	F	T
F	T	F
$\uparrow$		$\uparrow$

FIGURE 6.1

Example E. If p is *any* proposition then $\sim p \Leftrightarrow p$. This is also indicated in Figure 6.1.

Example F. If p and q are *any* propositions then $\sim (p \vee q) \Leftrightarrow \sim p \wedge \sim q$, as indicated in Figure 6.2. [Note that in the given equivalence "$\vee$" is on the left and "$\wedge$" is on the right.]

p	q	$p \vee q$	$\sim (p \vee q)$	$\sim p$	$\sim q$	$\sim p \wedge \sim q$
T	T	T	F	F	F	F
T	F	T	F	F	T	F
F	T	T	F	T	F	F
F	F	F	T	T	T	T
			$\uparrow$			$\uparrow$

FIGURE 6.2

Examples D, E, and F are particularly interesting. The equivalence or non-equivalence in these examples does not depend on the truth values of the component propositions, but only on symbolic form. This sort of equivalence is sometimes called *logical equivalence* or *equivalence of forms*. We can say that the forms $\sim(p \vee q)$ and $\sim p \wedge \sim q$ are equivalent, or, alternatively, if p and q are propositions, then the propositions $\sim(p \vee q)$ and $\sim p \wedge \sim q$ are logically equivalent. In practice we shall subsume both kinds of equivalence under the single word "equivalent."

Let us look at an example in which p and q are known propositions. Let p = "John likes meat" and q = "Mary likes fish." Then, from Example F we see that the negation of the proposition "John likes meat **or** Mary likes fish" is equivalent to the proposition "John does not like meat **and** Mary does not like fish." [It is possible to see this intuitively, without resorting to the truth table of Figure 6.2, but the truth table furnishes a convenient check.]

Let us consider a somewhat more complicated example.

Example G. Must $p \wedge (q \vee r)$ and $(p \wedge q) \vee (p \wedge r)$ be equivalent for *all* propositions p, q, and r?

Solution. Yes, as can be seen from Figure 6.3.

p	q	r	$q \vee r$	$p \wedge (q \vee r)$	$p \wedge q$	$p \wedge r$	$(p \wedge q) \vee (p \wedge r)$
T	T	T	T	T	T	T	T
T	T	F	T	T	T	F	T
T	F	T	T	T	F	T	T
T	F	F	F	F	F	F	F
F	T	T	T	F	F	F	F
F	T	F	T	F	F	F	F
F	F	T	T	F	F	F	F
F	F	F	F	F	F	F	F

FIGURE 6.3

Let us apply the result of Example G to particular propositions. Let p be "Patricia went to a play," let q be "Queenie went to a ball," and let r be "Ramona stayed home." Then $p \wedge (q \vee r)$ is "Patricia went to a play *and,* moreover, Queenie went to a ball *or* Ramona stayed home." On the other hand, $(p \wedge q) \vee (p \wedge r)$ is "Either Patricia went to a play *and* Queenie went to a ball, *or* Patricia went to a play and Ramona stayed home, *or* perhaps both." The result of Example G shows that the last two propositions are equivalent. [Again, it is possible to grasp the indicated equivalence intuitively, but the truth table furnishes an aid and a check.]

A final word. The result of Example G is that

$$p \wedge (q \vee r) \Leftrightarrow (p \wedge q) \vee (p \wedge r)$$

for all *propositions p, q,* and *r.* This symbolic statement resembles the well-known law

$$p \cdot (q + r) = p \cdot q + p \cdot r$$

of high-school algebra, which holds for all *numbers p, q,* and *r.* Here "$\wedge$" replaces "$\cdot$", "$\vee$" replaces "$+$", and "$\Leftrightarrow$" replaces "$=$". This resemblance suggests that some sort of algebraic manipulation might be possible with the subject matter of logic. This in fact is the case. There does exist an *algebra of propositions.* This algebra can be used to advantage in replacing complicated propositions or forms by equivalent propositions or forms which are easier to understand. Some indication of the possibilities was given in the above work, and further indications can be found in the exercises.

EXERCISES

1. Pick out two pairs of equivalent propositions from the following list:

   (a) $2 + 1 = 17$.
   (b) $2 + 2 = 4$.
   (c) The moon is made of green cheese.
   (d) The sun is made of polished brass.

2. The following statements are known as *De Morgan's rules* (for propositions):

   (a) *If p and q are any propositions then* $\sim(p \lor q) \Leftrightarrow \sim p \land \sim q$.
   (b) *If p and q are any propositions then* $\sim(p \land q) \Leftrightarrow \sim p \lor \sim q$.

   In Example F we showed that (a) is correct. By means of a truth table show that (b) is also correct.

3. In each of the following use De Morgan's rules to find an equivalent proposition and state this equivalent proposition in words.

   (a) It is false that (the night is young and you are beautiful).
   (b) It is false that (Joe is slow or Jane is plain).
   (c) It is false that (candy is dandy but [and] liquor is quicker).†
   (d) It is false that (the moon is blue or my bonnie lies over the ocean).

4. Show by means of a truth table that

   $$p \lor (q \land r) \Leftrightarrow (p \lor q) \land (p \lor r)$$

   for all propositions *p, q,* and *r.* Also, compare this result with that of Example G, above.

5. Use the result of Exercise 4 to "simplify" the following proposition: Patricia went to a play or Queenie went to a ball and, moreover, Patricia went to a play or Ramona stayed home.

6. (a) Find specific propositions *p, q,* and *r* for which

   $$p \land (q \lor r) \Leftrightarrow (p \land q) \lor r.$$

   (b) Find specific propositions *p, q,* and *r* for which

   $$p \land (q \lor r) \nLeftrightarrow (p \land q) \lor r.$$

---

† Apologies to Ogden Nash.

(c) Are the forms $p \wedge (q \vee r)$ and $(p \wedge q) \vee r$ equivalent? Defend your answer.

7. Suppose you know that Rod went to the races or Charlie played golf and, moreover, Rod went to the races or Charlie did not play golf. What can you conclude? Can you prove that your conclusion is correct?

8. Suppose you know that Jim went skiing and, moreover, Jim went skiing or Alice stayed home. What can you conclude? Can you prove that your conclusion is correct?

9. Assuming that the following is a meaningful proposition, show that it must be true: It is false that [triangle *ABC* is isosceles and, moreover (triangle *ABC* is not isosceles or quadrilateral *ABCD* is a parallelogram)] or quadrilateral *ABCD* is a parallelogram. Can you prove that your answer is correct?

*7. *The Algebra of Logic*

The object of the present section is to study an algebra which is closely related to the work we have been doing. This algebra, which we shall call the *algebra of logic,* is very similar to the algebra of propositions mentioned in the preceding section and can, in fact, serve the same purposes. The reason for studying the algebra of logic, rather than the algebra of propositions, is that it is simpler and more useful, and can serve as an excellent model for more general systems studied in abstract algebra and electrical engineering.

The algebra of logic is not the same as ordinary high-school algebra, but it does resemble high-school algebra to a certain extent. Ordinary high-school algebra is based on ordinary arithmetic. Each statement of this algebra in effect expresses a great many statements of arithmetic. For example, the equation

$$(x + y)(x - y) = x^2 - y^2$$

expresses the statements

$$(10 + 1)(10 - 1) = 10^2 - 1^2$$

and

$$(20 + 1)(20 - 1) = 20^2 - 1^2$$

as well as many others. Similarly, each statement of the algebra of logic expresses many statements of an "arithmetic" of another kind, an arithmetic of truth values. Let us examine this arithmetic briefly.

In the arithmetic of truth values the "numbers" are the two truth values T and F, and the "multiplication tables" are those of Figure 7.1. The first two of these tables are read like the ordinary multiplication table of Figure 7.2. Since there are only two objects (T and F) to deal with, calculations are very easy.

$\wedge$	T	F
T	T	F
F	F	F

(a)

$\vee$	T	F
T	T	T
F	T	F

(b)

$\sim T = F$

$\sim F = T$

(c)

FIGURE 7.1

$\times$	2	3	4	5	6	7	•	•	•
2	4	6	8	10	12	14	•	•	•
3	6	9	12	15	•	•	•	•	•
4	8	12	16	•	•	•	•	•	•
5	10	•	•	•	•	•	•	•	•
•	•	•	•	•	•	•	•	•	•
•	•	•	•	•	•	•	•	•	•
•	•	•	•	•	•	•	•	•	•

FIGURE 7.2

Example A. Calculate: $\sim(\sim F \wedge T)$.

Solution. $\sim(\sim F \wedge T) = \sim(T \wedge T) = \sim T = F$.

Example B. Calculate: $(\sim F \wedge T) \vee (F \wedge \sim T)$.

Solution.
$$(\sim F \wedge T) \vee (F \wedge \sim T) = (T \wedge T) \vee (F \wedge F)$$
$$= T \vee F = T.$$

Example C. Calculate: $(T \wedge F) \vee (\sim T \vee F)$.

Solution. $(T \wedge F) \vee (\sim T \vee F) = F \vee \sim T = F \vee F = F$.

Evidently, each calculation amounts only to a working through of a single line of a truth table. So much, therefore, for the "arithmetic" of truth values.

Let us now turn our attention to the "algebra" based on the foregoing arithmetic. Surprisingly, this algebra is fairly complicated —almost as complicated, in fact, as high-school algebra. As a beginning, we list a number of laws which we shall regard as basic. These laws may be proved directly by means of the truth table idea, and other laws may be derived from them. The selection of the following laws as *basic* was to some extent arbitrary. They were selected because they are frequently used, because their forms appear elsewhere in mathematics, and because all other laws of the algebra of logic can be derived from them.

In the following list each of the letters x, y, and z can stand for either of the truth values T, F. This practice is similar to that of high-school algebra, where letters can stand for numbers.

1. (a) $x \wedge \sim x = F$.
        $\sim x \wedge x = F$.
   (b) $x \vee \sim x = T$.
        $\sim x \vee x = T$.
   (c) $\sim \sim x = x$.

Note that each of these equations expresses *two* equations in the "arithmetic" of logic. For example, 1(c) says that $\sim \sim T = T$ and $\sim \sim F = F$. The above laws are called *complement laws,* because they indicate how a truth value x can combine with its "complement," $\sim x$.

2. (a) $x \wedge T = x.$
   $T \wedge x = x.$
   (b) $x \wedge F = F.$
   $F \wedge x = F.$
   (c) $x \vee T = T.$
   $T \vee x = T.$
   (d) $x \vee F = x.$
   $F \vee x = x.$

Laws 2(a) and 2(d) indicate how T and F allow a truth value x to retain its identity. For this reason T and F are called *identities* for $\wedge$ and $\vee$, respectively, and the above laws are called *identity laws*.

3. (a) $x \wedge x = x.$
   (b) $x \vee x = x.$ *Idempotent laws*

The word "idempotent" stems from the Latin *idem* (same) and *potentatus* (power).

4. (a) $x \wedge y = y \wedge x.$
   (b) $x \vee y = y \vee x.$ *Commutative laws*

5. (a) $\sim(x \wedge y) = \sim x \vee \sim y.$
   (b) $\sim(x \vee y) = \sim x \wedge \sim y.$ *De Morgan's rules*

Note the resemblance of laws 5(a) and (b) to the corresponding rules of Exercise 2 of the preceding section. De Morgan's rules are more complicated than laws 1 through 4, but also more useful.

6. (a) $(x \wedge y) \wedge z = x \wedge (y \wedge z).$
   (b) $(x \vee y) \vee z = x \vee (y \vee z).$ *Associative laws*

Conjunction ($\wedge$) has been defined only for *pairs* of truth values. Hence to find the conjunction of a *triple* of truth values one must form the conjunction of one truth value with the conjunction of the other two. The associative law for conjunction, law 6(a), states that two ways of finding the conjunction yield the same result. Similar remarks apply, of course, to the operation of disjunction ($\vee$).

7.   (a) $x \wedge (y \vee z) = (x \wedge y) \vee (x \wedge z)$.   *Distributive laws*
     (b) $x \vee (y \wedge z) = (x \vee y) \wedge (x \vee z)$.

We are now equipped to go through some manipulations in the algebra of logic. Do not be dismayed if you have trouble at first, because this kind of algebra is new. After a little practice the difficulties will vanish.

Example D.   Show from the above laws that $x \wedge (\sim x \vee x) = x$.

Solution. $x \wedge (\sim x \vee x) = x \wedge T$ by 1(b)
                  $= x$ by 2(a).

Of course, the given equation says that
$$T \wedge (\sim T \vee T) = T$$
and that $F \wedge (\sim F \vee F) = F$.

Example E.   Simplify: $\sim \sim x \vee F$.

Solution. $\sim \sim x \vee F = x \vee F = x$ by 1(c) and 2(d).

Example F.   Simplify: $x \vee (\sim x \vee y)$.

Solution. $x \vee (\sim x \vee y) = (x \vee \sim x) \vee y$ by 6(b)
                  $= T \vee y$ by 1(b)
                  $= T$ by 2(c).

Example G.   Simplify: $x \wedge (\sim x \vee y)$.

Solution. $x \wedge (\sim x \vee y) = (x \wedge \sim x) \vee (x \wedge y)$ by 7(a)
                  $= F \vee (x \wedge y)$ by 1(a)
                  $= x \wedge y$ by 2(d).

Example H.   Simplify: $\sim y \wedge [x \wedge (\sim x \vee y)]$.

Solution.

$$\sim y \wedge [x \wedge (\sim x \vee y)] = \sim y \wedge (x \wedge y) \qquad \text{by Example G}$$
$$= \sim y \wedge (y \wedge x) \qquad \text{by 4(a)}$$
$$= (\sim y \wedge y) \wedge x \qquad \text{by 6(a)}$$
$$= F \wedge x \qquad \text{by 1(a)}$$
$$= F \qquad \text{by 2(b).}$$

Many expressions do not simplify under manipulation, but only change form.

Example I. Manipulate: $(x \wedge \sim y) \vee (\sim x \wedge y)$.

Work: $(x \wedge \sim y) \vee (\sim x \wedge y)$.

$$= [(x \wedge \sim y) \vee \sim x] \wedge [(x \wedge \sim y) \vee y] \qquad \text{by 7(b)}$$
$$= [\sim x \vee (x \wedge \sim y)] \wedge [y \vee (x \wedge \sim y)] \qquad \text{by 4(b) (twice)}$$
$$= [(\sim x \vee x) \wedge (\sim x \vee \sim y)] \wedge [(y \vee x) \wedge (y \vee \sim y)]$$
$$\text{by 7(b) (twice)}$$
$$= [T \wedge (\sim x \vee \sim y)] \wedge [(y \vee x) \wedge T] \qquad \text{by 1(b) (twice)}$$
$$= (\sim x \vee \sim y) \wedge (y \vee x) \qquad \text{by 2(a) (twice)}$$
$$= [\sim (x \wedge y)] \wedge (y \vee x) \qquad \text{by 5(a).}$$

Results of this sort are sometimes useful. There are, for example, five symbols $(\wedge, \sim, \vee, \sim, \wedge)$ in the first expression of Example I, but only four in the last. As you will see, eliminations of this sort can mean economy of design of certain electrical networks. The reason for this is that the algebra of some networks is essentially the same as the algebra of logic.

EXERCISES

1. Calculate the value (T or F) of each of the following:

   (a) $(T \wedge \sim F) \vee (F \wedge \sim T)$.
   (b) $(\sim T \wedge F) \vee [F \wedge (T \vee F)]$.
   (c) $\sim [\sim (T \vee F) \wedge \sim (\sim T \vee F)] \wedge (F \vee T)$.

2. In each of the following, find which letter or letters (T or F) can be put into the box(es) to make the indicated "open"

equation a true statement. If more than one box appears in a problem, the same letter should go into each of the boxes. There may be no solution, one solution, or two solutions. [Proceed by trial and error. This is often the best way to solve equations.]

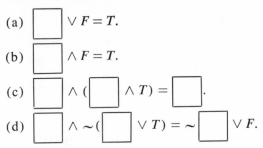

(a) $\square \vee F = T.$

(b) $\square \wedge F = T.$

(c) $\square \wedge (\square \wedge T) = \square.$

(d) $\square \wedge {\sim}(\square \vee T) = {\sim}\square \vee F.$

3. In the following, if you put one letter (T or F) into each of the square boxes and one letter into each of the round boxes, *must* you get a true statement?

$${\sim}(\square \vee \bigcirc) = {\sim}\square \wedge {\sim}\bigcirc$$

[There are four possibilities.]

4. Using the algebra of logic, simplify each of the following:

(a) $x \wedge (x \wedge x).$
(b) $x \wedge (x \wedge y).$
(c) ${\sim}x \wedge (x \wedge y).$
(d) ${\sim}({\sim}x \wedge y).$
(e) ${\sim}({\sim}x \vee {\sim}y).$
(f) ${\sim}x \vee (x \wedge y).$
(g) $(x \vee y) \wedge (x \vee {\sim}y).$
(h) ${\sim}(x \vee F) \vee (x \wedge T).$
(i) ${\sim}[x \wedge ({\sim}x \vee y)] \vee y.$
#(j) $x \wedge (x \vee y).$ *Hint:* $x = x \vee F.$
#(k) ${\sim}[({\sim}x \vee y) \wedge ({\sim}y \vee z)] \vee ({\sim}x \vee z).$

5. Suppose that $\rightarrow$ (read as "arrow") is a new operation having the property that $(x \rightarrow y) = {\sim}x \vee y$ for all truth values x and y.

(a) Find $F \to T$.

    Solution. $F \to T = \sim F \lor T = T \lor T = T$.

(b) Find $T \to F$.

(c) Find $T \to T$.

(d) Find $F \to F$.

6. If "$\to$" is as in Exercise 5, show that, for all truth values x and y,

  (a) $x \to T = T$.

  (b) $F \to x = T$.

  (c) $\sim (x \to y) = x \land \sim y$.

  (d) $(x \to y) \to (\sim y \to \sim x) = T$.

  (e) $x \to y$ does not always equal $y \to x$. That is, operation arrow is *not commutative*.

‡7. Restate Exercises 4(i) and 4(k) in terms of the arrow operation of Exercise 5. Then write the results of these exercises as theorems about the arrow operation.

8. Suppose that $\veebar$ (read as "exclusive or") is a new operation having the property that $x \veebar y = (x \lor y) \land \sim (x \land y)$ for all truth values x and y. Calculate each of the following:

  (a) $T \veebar T$.

  (b) $T \veebar F$.

  (c) $F \veebar T$.

  (d) $F \veebar F$.

9. If "$\veebar$" is as in Exercise 8, show that

  (a) $x \veebar x = F$.

  (b) $F \veebar x = x$. (*Identity law.*)

  (c) $T \veebar x = \sim x$.

  (d) $x \veebar y = y \veebar x$. (*Commutative law.*)

  (e) $x \veebar y = (x \land \sim y) \lor (\sim x \land y)$.

  (f) $x \veebar (y \veebar z) = (x \veebar y) \veebar z$. (*Associative law.*)

  (g) $x \land (y \veebar z) = (x \land y) \veebar (x \land z)$. (*Distributive law.*)

10. Find truth values x, y, and z for which

$$x \veebar (y \land z) \neq (x \veebar y) \land (x \veebar z).$$

[Your work will show that appearances may be deceiving—because although the equation

$$x \veebar (y \wedge z) = (x \veebar y) \wedge (x \veebar z)$$

looks like the equation

$$x \times (y + z) = (x \times y) + (x \times z)$$

it is not nearly as valid.]

♯11. An operation analogous to that of Exercise 8 can be defined for propositions. Guess its meaning.

*8. Black Boxes

You might be interested to know that the material you have studied is extremely important in the modern world. We cannot go into great detail concerning the reasons for this, but perhaps we can sketch a rough picture of one aspect of the situation.

For many centuries, one of the great needs of the world has been the need for arithmetic computation. Used in commerce, in navigation, and in innumerable other ways, plain, ordinary arithmetic has been essential to the proper functioning of civilization. And, as our civilization has become more complicated, the need for arithmetic computation has increased.

To make it possible to perform certain calculations in a reasonable time, and to ease the burden of carrying out other calculations, men have invented calculating machines. Nowadays almost all calculation is done by machine. This is not merely for the sake of convenience; it is necessary. Necessary, that is, if we are to live in a world of accurate weather prediction, automatic production, comprehensive communication, and artificial satellites.

Here is how logic fits in. In a modern digital computer, calculations are, to a large extent, carried through by special electronic circuits. And many of these circuits are electronic analogues of logical operations. In fact, a modern computer is, basically, a complicated logical machine. Our object here is to show how certain

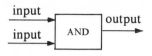

FIGURE 8.1

kinds of "hardware" can be used to perform logical operations. We shall not be interested in details of construction, nor can we show how this "hardware" can be used for calculation.

We shall use the term "black box" to designate any electrical— or electronic—analogue of a logical operation. We use this term because we are interested in the *function* of the devices concerned, rather than in their construction. Indeed, details of construction have changed rapidly with changing technology, while the essential function of the black boxes has remained the same.

The black box called "AND" works as follows: There are two "inputs" and one "output." [See Figure 8.1.] The box is so constructed that the output is "hot" when both inputs are hot, and "cold" otherwise. Thus the AND box works like the operation $\wedge$, a hot input corresponding to T and a cold input corresponding to F. [If you have had no experience with "hot" electricity, you can obtain such experience free of charge from any mischievous electrician.]

The OR box also has two inputs and one output. The output is hot unless both inputs are cold. The NOT box has one input and one output. The output of the NOT box is cold when the input is hot, and hot when the input is cold. The accompanying sketches

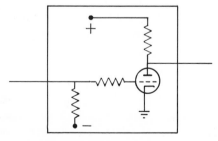

NOT box using vacuum tube

FIGURE 8.2

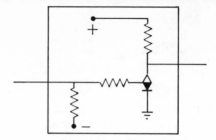

NOT box using transistor

FIGURE 8.3

Power supply for NOT box

FIGURE 8.4

(Figures 8.2 to 8.4) might be useful to the student interested in specific details of operation. For our purposes, however, we shall not need to know what actually happens inside any of the black boxes.

With the aid of black boxes we can readily construct networks which act as truth tables for particular logical operations. For example, a network analogous to $(x \land \sim y) \lor z$ is given in Figure 8.5(c). Figures 8.5(a) and (b) show two stages of construction. The output A in this figure is hot when X is hot and Y is cold, or when Z is hot. Otherwise A is cold. Analogously, $(x \land \sim y) \lor z$

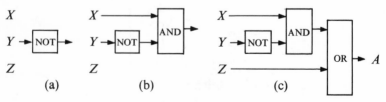

FIGURE 8.5

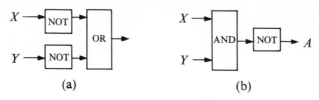

FIGURE 8.6

$= T$ when $x = T$ and $y = F$, or when $z = T$. Otherwise $(x \wedge \sim y)$ $\vee z = F$.

The algebra of logic given in the preceding section can be applied directly to networks of black boxes. This often results in a reduction in the number of components needed in such networks. For example, the two networks of Figure 8.6 act in exactly the same way, because $\sim (x \wedge y) = \sim x \vee \sim y$.

One possible immediate application of black boxes is to the problem of the hall light. A "hall light" is a lamp which is hooked up so that it can be controlled from any one of several locations. Such hookups are most commonly associated with long corridors. We wish to control the operation of a hall light from two given locations at the ends of the hall. A network which will do the job is given in Figure 8.7. The switches are at X and Y. When X and Y are both hot or both cold the light L is on. Otherwise the light is off. Obviously either switch can turn the light off and on.

The problem of designing the hall light network is clearly the same as that of designing the expression $(x \wedge y) \vee (\sim x \wedge \sim y)$. This problem will be treated in the next section.

In actual practice the hall light problem is not solved in the

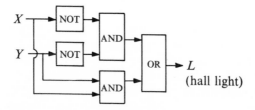

FIGURE 8.7

manner indicated, because there is a much cheaper solution. This solution will be discussed in the section on switching networks. It will be noted there, however, that the principles involved are essentially the same in both cases.

EXERCISES

1. Draw a diagram for each of the following networks:

   (a) $(X$ AND $Y)$ OR X.
   (b) $(X$ AND $Y)$ OR (NOT $X)$.
   (c) $(X$ OR $Y)$ AND (NOT X OR $Y)$.
   (d) $(X$ AND $Y)$ OR $(X$ AND $Z)$.
   (e) $(X$ OR $Y)$ AND (NOT X AND NOT $Y)$.

2. Find a black box hall light network which requires fewer black boxes than the one given in the text (Figure 8.7).

3. For each of the following find an equivalent network which uses fewer black boxes:

   (a) $(X$ OR $Y)$ AND (NOT X OR $Y)$.
   (b) $(X$ AND $Y)$ OR $(X$ AND $Z)$.
   (c) NOT (NOT X OR NOT $Y)$.
   (d) NOT $[X$ AND (NOT X OR $Y)]$ OR Y.
   (e) NOT (NOT X AND NOT $Y)$.
   (f) (NOT X AND NOT $Y)$ OR $(X$ OR $Y)$.

*9. Logical Design

In any branch of technology, activity may be classified into two broad categories. In one of these the main concern is with things that already exist, and in the other it is with the design and development of something new. This section will be concerned with the latter kind of activity as it pertains to problems of logical design. Although strictly academic, the hall light problem of the preceding section is representative of a number of problems of this sort. In these problems we wish to control the output (to the light, for example) by means of a number of inputs (as at the switches).

Abstractly speaking, we are confronted with the problem of designing a black box having specified properties.

Before beginning, we make a few abbreviations. In what follows the letter "T" will stand for "hot" (easily remembered by the "T" in "Torrid"), "F" will stand for "cold" ("Frigid"), "$\wedge$" will stand for "AND," and so on. These abbreviations will allow us to apply the algebra of logic already studied.

We begin our study of design with the simplest possible case—that in which there is only one input. In this case there are precisely four ways of obtaining the output. The output can agree or disagree with the input, or be totally indifferent to the input. The former possibilities are given in Figures 9.1(b) and (c), and the latter in Figures 9.1(a) and (d). In these figures "X" represents

X	A
T	T
F	T
(a)	

X	A
T	T
F	F
(b)	

X	A
T	F
F	T
(c)	

X	A
T	F
F	F
(d)	

FIGURE 9.1

the input and "A" the output. The solutions of the problems posed by these tables can be written down immediately:

(a) $A = T$.   (c) $A = \sim X$.

(b) $A = X$.   (d) $A = F$.

Black boxes corresponding to each of these solutions are easily constructed. In (a), for example, merely let A be hot, or alternatively let $A = X \vee \sim X$ as in Figure 9.2.

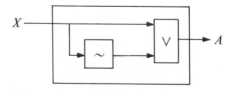

FIGURE 9.2

Next in level of difficulty is the case in which there are two inputs. This case can also be treated by listing all possibilities, but it is better to use more general ideas.

Consider the following four basic forms: $X \wedge Y$, $X \wedge \sim Y$, $X \wedge Y$, and $\sim X \wedge \sim Y$. Each of these forms has a table with exactly one "T" in its final column, as shown in Figure 9.3. From

X	Y	$X \wedge Y$
T	T	T
T	F	F
F	T	F
F	F	F

(a)

X	Y	$X \wedge \sim Y$
T	T	F
T	F	T
F	T	F
F	F	F

(b)

X	Y	$\sim X \wedge Y$
T	T	F
T	F	F
F	T	T
F	F	F

(c)

X	Y	$\sim X \wedge \sim Y$
T	T	F
T	F	F
F	T	F
F	F	T

(d)

FIGURE 9.3

this it should be clear that a *form for any particular operation* (with at least one T in the final column of its table) *can be constructed by taking disjunctions of these basic forms.* If A has the table of Figure 9.4, for example, then $A = (X \wedge \sim Y) \vee (\sim X \wedge Y)$. Or, in general, a form for any operation with a

X	Y	A
T	T	F
T	F	T
F	T	T
F	F	F

FIGURE 9.4

column containing two "*T*"s can be formed as a disjunction of two of the basic forms. Similarly, if *A* has three "*T*"s in its final column, then *A* is a disjunction of three of the basic forms of Figure 9.3, and so on. In the exceptional case where *A* is always cold, we can write "$A = X \wedge \sim X$."

The method we have described can be applied to the design of black boxes having any number of inputs. For three inputs there are eight basic operations: $X \wedge Y \wedge Z$, $X \wedge Y \wedge \sim Z$, etc. [Note that a black box for $X \wedge Y \wedge Z$ can be made from two AND boxes: $X \wedge Y \wedge Z = X \wedge (Y \wedge Z)$.]

Now let us apply our work to the hall light problem. The chief difficulty with this problem, as with many others, is to *state the problem properly*. [Many mathematicians feel that a problem well stated is at least half solved.] If we assume that the light *A* is on (*T*) when both inputs *X* and *Y* are hot (*T*) then each single change of *X* or *Y* changes *A*. In this case our table must be as in Figure 9.5. If we assume that $A = F$ when $X = Y = T$ we obtain the table of Figure 9.4. So the problem is to design a form which has the table of Figure 9.4 or of Figure 9.5. The solution is now

X	*Y*	*A*
T	*T*	*T*
T	*F*	*F*
F	*T*	*F*
F	*F*	*T*

FIGURE 9.5

easy: The desired black box can be constructed from the formula

$$A = (X \wedge Y) \vee (\sim X \wedge \sim Y)$$

or the formula

$$A = (X \wedge \sim Y) \vee (\sim X \wedge Y).$$

It is important to realize that the solution obtained in the above manner need not be the one with the fewest components or inputs. Actually there is no known method for obtaining these "best" or most economical solutions automatically; but in most cases the derived solution can be simplified considerably by trial and error methods based on the algebra of logic.

EXERCISES

1. If A, B, C, D, E, F, and G have the following truth tables, express each in terms of X, Y, $\wedge$, $\vee$, and $\sim$. (Figure 9.6.)

X	Y	A	B	C	D	E	F	G
T	T	F	F	F	F	T	T	T
T	F	T	F	F	T	F	T	T
F	T	F	T	F	T	T	F	T
F	F	F	F	T	T	T	T	F

FIGURE 9.6

2. List all eight of the basic forms involving three inputs.

3. If A, B, and C have the following truth tables, express each in terms of X, Y, Z, $\wedge$, $\vee$, and $\sim$. (Figure 9.7.)

X	Y	Z	A	B	C
T	T	T	T	F	T
T	T	F	F	F	F
T	F	T	F	T	F
T	F	F	F	F	T
F	T	T	T	F	T
F	T	F	F	T	F
F	F	T	F	F	F
F	F	F	F	T	T

FIGURE 9.7

4. Two people play the game of matching pennies as follows: Both flip pennies simultaneously. If both pennies land heads or both land tails, player 1 wins. If one lands heads and the other tails then player 2 wins.

   (a) Write a truth table of a black box for playing an electrical analogue of this game.

(b) Express the output of such a box in terms of the inputs and the standard black boxes.

5. Election to a certain exclusive club requires the approval of all three members of the club's committee on memberships. A member indicates approval by dropping a white ball into a bag and disapproval by dropping a black ball. The presence of one or more black balls indicates that the candidate is not elected.

(a) Write a truth table of a black box by which this "black-balling" can be done electrically.
(b) Express the output of such a box in terms of the inputs and the standard black boxes.

6. The game of "odd man" is played as follows: Three people each flip a coin. If all three coins land heads or all three land tails, the game is a draw. Otherwise the winner is the man whose coin lands heads when the other two land tails, or tails when the other two land heads.

(a) Write a truth table of a black box for playing an electrical analogue of this game. This box is to have three inputs and three outputs. Each input should correspond to one output, and each output to one input. A hot output then indicates that the corresponding input is different from the other two inputs.
(b) Express each output of such a box in terms of the inputs and the standard black boxes.

♯7. Show that an AND box may be constructed from OR and NOT boxes.

♯8. The operation D of Exercise 1 is called *stroke*. This operation is written as "$X \mid Y$."

(a) Show how a STROKE box can be used as a substitute for a NOT box.
(b) Show how two STROKE boxes can be used as a substitute for an AND box.

*10. Switching Networks

The design principles of the preceding section have applications beyond the subject of black boxes. In this section we will see how they apply to electrical networks called *switching networks*. Among the results will be the practical economical solution of the hall light problem promised earlier.

A *switching network* is an arrangement of wires and switches connecting two terminals. The components of switching networks are familiar objects of everyday experience, so no detailed descriptions are necessary. It will be helpful, however, to note that the switches of everyday experience are frequently *multiple* switches; that is, collections of switches connected in such a way that several are controlled with one flick. Switches which operate three-way lamps are of this sort.

We will think of a switch as having two possible states of existence: "open" and "closed." A closed switch permits the passage of current, and an open switch does not. [See Figure 10.1.] Switching networks, too, have these two possible states of existence.

Open switch   Closed switch

FIGURE 10.1

Two switches, S_1 and S_2, may be connected as in Figure 10.2. [In (b) S_1 is open and S_2 is closed.] This sort of arrangement is known as a *series connection*. The wires and switches connecting terminal A to terminal B constitute a switching network. In order for this network to be closed, both S_1 and S_2 must be closed; other-

A ——— S_1 ——— S_2 ——— B A ——— S_1 —•—•— S_2 —•— B

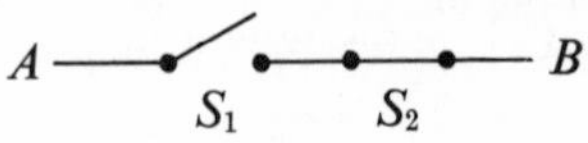

(a)   (b)

FIGURE 10.2

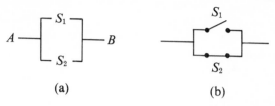

(a)   **(b)**

FIGURE 10.3

wise the network is open. The analogy with the logical operation of conjunction ($\wedge$) is obvious.

A *parallel connection* is an arrangement such as that of Figure 10.3. [In (b) S_1 is open and S_2 is closed.] This network is closed if S_1 is closed or S_2 is closed. Otherwise it is open. This connection is the analogue of the logical operation of disjunction ($\vee$).

Figure 10.4 shows a switching network composed of three switches, S_1, S_2, and S_3. This network is closed if S_3 is closed and either S_1 or S_2 is closed.

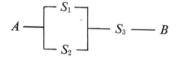

FIGURE 10.4

We have mentioned multiple switches. If several switches of a multiple switch open and close simultaneously, these switches are said to be *equivalent*. Now we are interested more in the *states* of switches (open or closed) than we are in the switches themselves. We could introduce something like the truth-value function τ of Section 3 to distinguish switches from their states, but we shall not do so. Instead, we shall tolerate slight ambiguities and use the same letter to designate a switch and its state. Thus equivalent switches will be designated by the same letter.

Among multiple switches there are arrangements whereby one switch is open while another is closed, and closed while the other is open. If one of these switches (or its state) is designated as "S," the other will be designated as "S'." Thus $(S')'$ has the same state as S. That is, $(S')' = S$. The analogy with the operation of negation is obvious.

The analogy with the logical apparatus so far developed is complete. We are thus in position to solve many problems associated with switching networks. In addition, we can simplify a number of expressions in the algebra of logic by means of switches. Thus the connection between logic and switching networks can go both ways.

At this point it is convenient to press our logical notation into service. With this notation the network of Figure 10.4 is represented simply as "$(S_1 \lor S_2) \land S_3$." This notation makes it easy to solve problems involving switching networks.

In our first attempt we note that the network of Figure 10.4 has the same electrical properties as that of Figure 10.5, because $(S_1 \lor S_2) \land S_3 = (S_1 \land S_3) \lor (S_2 \land S_3)$ in the algebra of logic. Thus the algebra of logic can be used for simplification (or complication!) purposes.

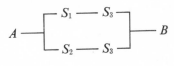

FIGURE 10.5

Next we design a practical hall-light network. The formal work of the preceding section applies directly. Reinterpreted in terms of switches, one solution is given by the expression

$$(S_1 \land S_2) \lor (S_1' \land S_2').$$

A complete circuit, including hall light and source of current, is given in Figure 10.6. Other applications will be found in the exercises.

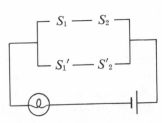

FIGURE 10.6

EXERCISES

1. Draw a diagram for each of the following switching networks:

   (a) $(S_1 \wedge S_2) \vee S_1'$.
   (b) $(S_1 \vee S_2) \wedge (S_1' \vee S_2)$.
   (c) $(S_1 \wedge S_2) \vee (S_1 \wedge S_3)$.
   (d) $[(S_1 \wedge S_2) \vee (S_1' \wedge S_2)] \vee (S_1 \wedge S_2')$.

2. Draw a pair of switching networks to illustrate each of the following laws:

   (a) $S_1 \vee S_1 = S_1$.
   (b) $S_1 \vee (S_2 \wedge S_3) = (S_1 \vee S_2) \wedge (S_1 \vee S_3)$.

3. Write an expression for each of the networks of Figure 10.7.

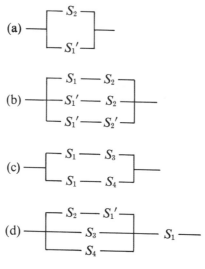

FIGURE 10.7

4. (a) Show by the algebra of logic that the networks of Exercises 3(a) and 3(b) are electrically equivalent.
   (b) Do the same for Exercises 3(c) and 3(d).

5. Design an effective hall-light network employing three switches and draw a diagram of your solution.

6. Design an effective network for indicating a majority vote. Assume that three people vote. Draw a diagram of your solution.

Part II

Sets and Logic

1. Sets and Subsets

One of the characteristics of twentieth-century mathematics is its constant and conscious use of the concept of *set* (or *class,* or *collection*). This concept is an abstraction from everyday experience: The automobiles on a street, the letters in the alphabet, and the children in a family all constitute sets. The individual automobiles, letters, and children are the *elements,* or *members,* of the given sets.

Although commonplace, the concept of set plays a fundamental role in mathematics. In geometry, for example, every circle and every straight line is a set of points. Again, in algebra the solutions of equations often come in sets. From these examples it should be clear that sets need not consist of concrete objects, but may include abstractions as well. Sets may even consist of events. With each proposed experiment, for example, we can associate a set of possible ways in which the experiment might turn out. In fact, this idea of a set of outcomes is fundamental in the mathematical theory of probability.

The concept of set is important in other places besides mathematics. In calling young men to military service, governments give special attention to particular sets of men; in mass production of automobiles interest is focused on sets of automobiles rather than on the isolated "lemons"; in census work the problem is to sort people into sets rather than to explore the characteristics of any one person.

Note that it is possible for sets themselves to be elements of other sets. This is a common idea: We list as examples the set of all minority groups, the set of all human families, and the set of all

45

labor unions. The individual minority groups, families, and labor unions are elements of sets; and they themselves are also sets.

Do not construe from the foregoing that the elements of a set must be related to one another in some simple, common way: Often the only obvious feature common to all members of a set is that they all belong to the same set! From this point of view a perfectly good set is that consisting of the letter "*K*," the moon, and the number 9.

We shall use the symbol " $\in$ " to indicate membership in a set and " $\notin$ " to indicate non-membership. Here are examples of how these symbols are used. Suppose that *A* is the set of all positive integers from 10 to 100, inclusive. To indicate that 43 is an element of this set we may write "43 $\in$ *A*." [Read "43 $\in$ *A*" as "43 is an element of *A*."] And, to indicate that 176 is not an element of *A* we may write "176 $\notin$ *A*."

Sometimes a set may be described completely by listing or naming its elements. We shall adopt a brace notation for this purpose. In this notation "{1, 2, 3, 4, 5}" denotes the set consisting of the first five positive integers. The order of listing the elements is immaterial. Thus the set just mentioned can also be denoted as "{1, 4, 3, 5, 2}."

It is awkward to list all the elements of very large sets. Sometimes, however, a set may be described in another way, by means of a condition which is satisfied by the elements of the set and by no others. The condition of being red, for example, defines the set of all red things. Again, the condition of being married defines the set of all married people. Needless to say, it is impossible to list all the elements of either of these sets. Yet they can be described, as we have just demonstrated.

If *A* and *B* are sets which are so related that every element of *A* is also an element of *B*, then *A* is said to be a *subset of B*, or to be *included in B*. Thus the set of all girls is a subset of the set of all people, and {1, 2, 4} is a subset of {1, 2, 3, 4, 5}. We shall write "*A* $\subseteq$ *B*" to indicate that *A* is a subset of *B*, and "*A* $\nsubseteq$ *B*" to indicate that *A* is not a subset of *B*. If *A* is included in *B*, then *B includes A*. This we can write as "*B* $\supseteq$ *A*."

Every set is a subset of itself. This follows from our definition

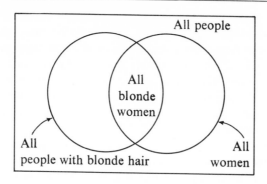

All people

All
blonde
women

All
people with blonde hair

All
women

FIGURE 1.1

of subset. Any subset of a set which is not the set itself is called
a *proper subset* of the set. To indicate that *A* is a proper subset of
B we write "*A* ⊂ *B*" ("*A* is properly included in *B*") or "*B* ⊃ *A*"
("*B* properly includes *A*").

Example A. The set {1, 2} is a proper subset of {1, 2, 3}. The
set {1, 2, 3} is a subset of {1, 2, 3} but not a proper subset.

In each of many discussions all sets are subsets of one particular
set. This set is called the *universal set* for that discussion. It may
change from discussion to discussion: The set of all natural numbers is usually the universal set in a discussion of natural numbers,
and the set of all people is the universal set of many discussions
in the cafeteria. Although universal sets are usually introduced as
a matter of convenience, there is a deeper reason for their existence. It has been found that indiscriminate use of conditions to
describe sets can lead to embarrassing logical paradoxes.† These
paradoxes can be avoided in a number of ways. The simplest way
is to restrict the applicability of conditions to specific universal
sets. This is the course we shall take. In the sequel, then, all sets
involved in a particular discussion will be subsets of a universal
set *U*, and we shall not be concerned with the paradoxes.

---

† Details can be found in many texts in logic under the heading of Russell's
paradox.

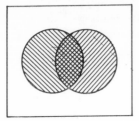 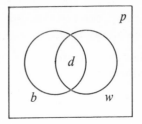

p: all people
w: all women
etc.

FIGURE 1.2

Subsets of a set can be visualized conveniently with the aid of diagrams commonly known as *Venn diagrams*. These represent sets as portions of a plane. When one set is a subset of another, the portion representing the one set is inside the portion representing the other. This device is illustrated in Figure 1.1. For convenience the various regions of the figure may be shaded, or in complicated cases designated with letters or numerals, as in Figure 1.2.

EXERCISES

1. Determine which of the following statements are true, and which are false:

    (a) $2 \in \{1, 2, 3, 4\}$.
    (b) $5 \in \{1, 2, 3\}$.
    (c) $3 \in S$, where S is the set of all even numbers.
    (d) $3 \notin T$, where T is the set of all odd numbers.
    (e) {Caesar, Napoleon} $\subset$ {Caesar, Napoleon, Chaplin}.
    (f) {Caesar, Napoleon, Chaplin} $\subset$ {Caesar, Napoleon, Chaplin}.
    (g) {Caesar, Napoleon} $\subseteq$ {Caesar, Napoleon, Chaplin}.

2. Is {France, Britain} a proper subset of the Security Council of the United Nations? Is {U.S.S.R.}?

3. Using brace notation, list all the subsets of the set $\{1, 2, 3\}$ which have exactly two elements. How many are there?

4. How many subsets of the set $\{1, 2, 3, 4, 5\}$ have exactly two elements?

5. Construct a single Venn diagram to illustrate the following subsets of the set of all people: All residents of Canada, all people of German descent, all people of Scottish descent. Indicate which set you take as the universal set.

6. Construct a single Venn diagram to illustrate the following subsets of the set of all people: All freshmen, all students, all beautiful girls, all engineering students. Indicate which set you take as the universal set.

7. In a group of 17 people 5 prefer their coffee black (with neither cream nor sugar), 8 take cream with their coffee, and 10 take sugar. They all drink coffee. What is a suitable universal set? How many people in the group take both cream and sugar? *Hint:* Draw a Venn diagram.

8. Given the "open" equation

$$\boxed{}^2 + 22 = 13 \times \boxed{} :$$

   (a) Find the set of all positive integers from 1 to 5 inclusive which, when placed into the boxes, turns this "open" equation into a *false* proposition. [The same number must go into both boxes.] Use braces. [An excellent way to do this problem is by trying each number in turn.]

   (b) Find the set of all numbers which, when placed in the boxes, turns this "open" equation into a *true* proposition. [There are two such numbers.] Use braces.

9. Repeat Exercise 8, but for the "open" equation

$$\boxed{}^3 + \boxed{} + 6 = 4 \times \boxed{}^2 .$$

[There are three numbers for (b).]

10. State a condition which determines membership in each of the following sets. [There is at least one correct answer to each of these exercises; there may be several.]

  (a) $\{1, 2, 3, 4, 5, 6, 7, 8, 9\}$.
  (b) $\{2, 3, 5, 7\}$.
  (c) {blue, red, yellow}.
  (d) {blue, red, white}.
  (e) {the moon, 9, "K"}.

2. *The Set Builder*

We have noted that a set may be described in two ways. One is to list all the elements of the set. The other is to state a condition which is satisfied by the elements of the set and by no others. In the preceding section we adopted a brace notation for use with the first method. In the present section we shall develop a convenient notation for use with the second.

First, let us look at a numerical example. Consider the equation "$x^4 + 4 = 5x^2$." This equation is satisfied by certain real numbers, but not by all. For example, it is satisfied by the number 1, because $1^4 + 4 = 5 \times 1^2$, but not by the number 3, because $3^4 + 4 \neq 5 \times 3^2$. Now the numbers that do satisfy the equation constitute a set, and a convenient way to *denote* this set is as

$$\{x \in R: x^4 + 4 = 5x^2\},$$

where R is the set of all real numbers. [Read this as "the set of all x in R such that $x^4 + 4 = 5x^2$."] It can be shown that the set of all (real number) solutions of the above equation is the set $\{-1, 1, 2, -2\}$. Thus

$$\{x \in R: x^4 + 4 = 5x^2\} = \{-1, 1, 2, -2\}.$$

As another example, we can *denote* the set of all solutions of the equation "$x^3 = 9x^2 + 6x - 12$" as

$$\{x \in R: x^3 = 9x^2 + 6x - 12\}.$$

In this case the set of solutions is not so easily listed.

Next, let us consider a non-numerical example. Suppose that we are talking about the set P of all people. Then the set of all strong people is defined by the condition of being strong, and can be denoted as

$$\{x \in P: x \text{ is strong}\}.$$

Similarly, the set of all beautiful people is defined by the condition of being beautiful, and can be denoted as

$$\{x \in P: x \text{ is beautiful}\}.$$

In general, let M be a set and let $p(x)$ be an "open" statement involving an unspecified term "x." If $p(x)$ becomes a proposition when a name of an element of M is substituted for "x" then we write

$$\{x \in M: p(x)\}$$

(or "$\{x: p(x)\}$" when M is clearly known) to denote the set of all elements of M for which $p(x)$ becomes a true proposition. Thus $\{x \in M: p(x)\}$ is the set of all elements of M that satisfy the statement $p(x)$. This set is known as the *truth set*, in M, of $p(x)$. Similarly, for each condition q, the set of all elements of M that satisfy the condition q is called the *truth set* of q and is denoted as "$\{x \in M: q(x)\}$" or "$\{y \in M: q(y)\}$", etc.

The symbol "$\{\ldots \in \ldots : \ldots\ldots\}$" is known as the *set builder*. It is a standard device for denoting sets defined by conditions. It is especially useful in mathematical discourse, where conditions are most often expressed as "open" statements involving unspecified terms such as "x." [For example, equations.]

Example A. Suppose that U is the set of all cities in North America and p is the condition of having had a population of over a million people in 1950. What is the truth set, in U, of p?

Solution. The desired truth set is $\{x \in U: p(x)\}$

$= x \in U$: the population of x was over a million people in 1950$\}$

$= \{$Chicago, Detroit, Los Angeles, Mexico City, Montreal, New York, Philadelphia$\}$.

Example B. Suppose that $\mathcal{N}$ is the set of all positive integers (whole numbers) and p is the condition of being less than 8. What is the truth set of p in $\mathcal{N}$?

Solution. The desired truth set is $\{x \in \mathcal{N}: p(x)\} = \{1, 2, 3, 4, 5, 6, 7\}$. We may also write this as "$\{x \in \mathcal{N}: x < 8\}$." [The symbol "$<$" means "is less than."]

Example C. If $\mathcal{N}$ is as in Example B find $\{z \in \mathcal{N}: z^2 = z + 2\}$.

Solution. $\{2\}$. [It is not $\{2, -1\}$ even though -1 satisfies the equation. The reason is that -1 is not an element of $\mathcal{N}$.]

Before going on, we must clarify an issue presented by the introduction of the set builder: What happens when no element of a set satisfies a given condition? If M is the set $\{1, 2, 3\}$ then the condition, in M, of being greater than 5 yields the "set" $\{x \in M: x \text{ is greater than } 5\}$; but this "set" has no elements.

So as to allow every condition to determine a set we introduce a new set called the *empty set*.† This set is defined by the condition that it have no elements; it is denoted as "$\varnothing$." The introduction of the empty settles questions such as that raised in the preceding paragraph: The set of all numbers greater than 5 in the set $M = \{1, 2, 3\}$ is the empty set. In symbols, $\{x \in M: x > 5\} = \varnothing$. The set of all five-legged bipeds is also the empty set.

You might find the empty set bizarre at first (just as early mathematicians found the number zero to be bizarre), but you will appreciate its convenience as you go along. The empty set is, in fact, used throughout present-day mathematics.

Given any set M, we expect every set of the form $\{x \in M: p(x)\}$ to be a subset of M. Since the empty set is of this form ($\varnothing = \{x \in M: x \neq x\}$) we shall consider the empty set to be a subset of every set. In particular, the empty set will be a subset of itself.

A final word of caution. In many of the foregoing examples conditions were expressed in the form of statements involving an

---

† Other names for the empty set are *null set, void set,* and *vacuous set.*

unspecified term "x." Here we must point out that sometimes such statements are not meant to express conditions—that is, are not "open"—but are meant as propositions about *specific* elements x. Thus a certain brand of margarine might be advertised as tasting as good as x, which is "that other table spread" or "you know what." In short, letters such as "x" can be used as *pronouns* (as in open statements) or as (proper) *nouns,* designating certain objects. Thus the notation "$p(x)$" is ambiguous, sometimes standing for an open statement and sometimes for a proposition. This ambiguity is widespread in mathematical discourse, but is tolerated for its linguistic convenience. The ambiguity is not serious, and causes no trouble to those who are fully aware of its existence.

EXERCISES

1. Let $\mathcal{N}$ be the set of all positive integers. List the elements of each of the following sets. Use braces.

    (a) $\{x \in \mathcal{N}: 8 = x + 3\}$.
    (b) $\{x \in \mathcal{N}: (x - 2)(x - 5) = 0\}$.
    (c) $\{x \in \mathcal{N}: x^2 + 22 = 13x\}$. [Compare this with Exercise 8(b) of the preceding section.]
    (d) $\{x \in \mathcal{N}: x^2 = 25\}$.
    (e) $\{x \in \mathcal{N}: (x - 1)(x - 2) = 12\}$.
    (f) $\{x \in \mathcal{N}: \sqrt{(5x - 1)} + \sqrt{(3x - 2)} = 3\}$.
    (g) $\{x \in \mathcal{N}: 2x < 9\}$.
    (h) $\{x \in \mathcal{N}: x + 5 < 3\}$.
    (i) $\{x \in \mathcal{N}: (x + 1)(x + 2) < 11\}$.

2. The record of the Boola College football team one season was as follows:

Boola	40	Podunk	2
Boola	19	Riverford	14
Boola	21	State	6
Boola	33	York	20
Boola	19	Tech	19
Boola	3	Ivy	6

Let F be the set of Boola's opponents that season. List the elements of the truth set, in F, of each of the following open statements. Use braces.

(a) Boola beat x.
(b) x beat Boola.
(c) Boola beat x by more than 14 points.
(d) x beat Boola by more than 14 points.
(e) x scored more than 14 points against Boola.

3. Let P be the set of all Pacific Coast states of continental United States. List the elements of each of the following sets. Use braces.

(a) $\{x \in P: x$ borders Nevada$\}$.
(b) $\{x \in P: x$ does not border Nevada$\}$.
(c) $\{x \in P: x$ borders Mexico$\}$.
(d) $\{x \in P: \sim (x$ borders Mexico$)\}$.
(e) $\{x \in P: x$ has an international boundary$\}$.
(f) $\{x \in P: x$ is smaller than Texas$\}$.
(g) $\{x \in P: x$ is larger than Texas$\}$.
(h) $\{x \in P: x$ is in New England$\}$.

4. Let L be the set of all Great Lakes. List the elements of the truth sets, in L, of each of the following open statements. Use braces.

(a) x borders Ontario.
(b) x is entirely within the United States.
(c) x borders New York State.
(d) x has fresh water.
(e) x borders Nevada.
(f) x borders Michigan.

5. Eleven cities of the Western Hemisphere having large populations in their metropolitan areas are New York, Chicago, Buenos Aires, Los Angeles, Philadelphia, Mexico City, Sao Paulo, Rio de Janeiro, Montreal, Boston, and San Francisco. Let C be the set of all these cities. List the elements of each of the following sets. Use braces.

(a) $\{x \in C: x$ was the capital of a country in 1950$\}$.
(b) $\{x \in C: x$ has a harbor$\}$.
(c) $\{x \in C: x$ has English as an official language$\}$.
(d) $\{x \in C: x$ has French as an official language$\}$.
(e) $\{x \in C: x$ has Italian as an official language$\}$.
(f) $\{x \in C: x$ has Portuguese as an official language$\}$.
(g) $\{x \in C: x$ has Spanish as an official language$\}$.
(h) $\{x \in C: x$ had a population of over two million people in 1950$\}$.

6. According to convention, does the empty set have any subsets? If so, how many?

7. List all the subsets of each of the following sets, and determine the total number in each case:

    (a) $\{1\}$.
    (b) $\{1, 2\}$.
    (c) $\{1, 2, 3\}$.

8. If $M = \{1, 2, 3, 4\}$ find $\{x \in M: x \notin \varnothing\}$.

♯9. If a set has four elements, how many subsets does it have? What if it has five elements? Six? Ten?

10. One year a certain professor found that all of his students dropped his course before the term was half over. After the last student had left, did the professor still have a class?

3. *Operations on Sets*

We have seen that a set may be described by means of an open statement which is satisfied by the elements of the set and by no others. Now open statements, like propositions, may be combined with the words *and, or,* and *not* to yield other open statements. It is worthwhile examining the effect of such combinations on the *sets* defined by these open statements.

Let A and B be subsets of a universal set $\mathcal{U}$. We shall define the *intersection* of A and B to be the set of all elements of $\mathcal{U}$ which belong to both A and B. The intersection of A and B will be denoted as "$A \cap B$." Formally,

$$A \cap B = \{x \in \mathcal{U}: (x \in A) \wedge (x \in B)\}.$$

The symbol "$\cap$" is read as "cap" or "intersection."

Example A. Let $\mathcal{U}$ be the set of all people, let W be the set of all women, and let B be the set of all people with blonde hair. What is $B \cap W$?

Solution. The set of all women with blonde hair. [See Figure 1.1.]

Example B. Let $\mathcal{U}$ be the set of all people, let P be the set of all politicians, and let H be the set of all honest people. What is $H \cap P$?

Solution. The set of all honest politicians. [Some cynics say that this set is empty.]

The operation of intersection corresponds to the logical operation **and.** Corresponding to **or** is the operation of *union.* The *union* of subsets A and B of a universal set $\mathcal{U}$ is the set of all elements of $\mathcal{U}$ that belong to A *or* to B (or to both A and B). The union of A and B will be denoted as "$A \cup B$." Formally,

$$A \cup B = \{x \in \mathcal{U}: (x \in A) \vee (x \in B)\}.$$

The symbol "$\cup$" is read as "cup" or "union."

Example C. Let $\mathcal{U}$ be the set of all people, let K be the set of all knaves, and let F be the set of all fools. What is $K \cup F$?

Solution. The set of all people who are either knaves or fools (or both).

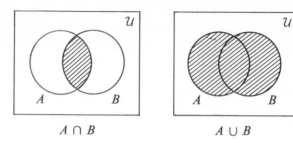

$A \cap B$ $A \cup B$

FIGURE 3.1

Example D. Find $A \cap B$ and $A \cup B$ if $A = \{1, 3, 5, 7, 9\}$ and $B = \{2, 3, 5, 7\}$.

Solution. $A \cap B = \{3, 5, 7\}$ and $A \cup B = \{1, 2, 3, 5, 7, 9\}$.

Venn diagrams for the operations of intersection and union appear in Figure 3.1. These diagrams illustrate only the case in which A and B have at least one element in common; that is, in which A and B *intersect* or *overlap*. If A and B have no elements in common then $A \cap B = \varnothing$, and conversely. In this case A and B are said to be *disjoint*.

The last operation to be discussed here is that of taking the *complement* of a set. This corresponds to the logical operation **not**. The *complement* of a subset A of a universal set $\mathcal{U}$ is the set of all elements of $\mathcal{U}$ which are *not* in A. The complement of A will be denoted as "A'." Formally,

$$A' = \{x \in \mathcal{U}: \sim(x \in A)\}.$$

[Read "A'" as "A prime."] For example, if $\mathcal{U} = \{1, 2, 3, 4, 5\}$ and $A = \{1, 4\}$, then $A' = \{2, 3, 5\}$. Again, if $\mathcal{U}$ is the set of all people and M is the set of all married people then M' is the set of all unmarried people. Complements are illustrated in Figure 3.2.

Finally, we note the effect of the above operations on truth sets of open statements. Let P and Q be the truth sets, in a universal set $\mathcal{U}$, of open statements $p(x)$ and $q(x)$, respectively. Then it

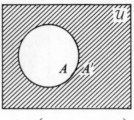

$$A' = \{ x \in \mathcal{U} : x \notin A \}$$

FIGURE 3.2

can be shown that $P \cap Q$ is the truth set of the open statement $p(x) \wedge q(x)$. Thus

$$P \cap Q = \{x : p(x)\} \cap \{x : q(x)\}$$
$$= \{x : p(x) \wedge q(x)\}.$$

Similarly,

$$P \cup Q = \{x : p(x)\} \cup \{x : q(x)\}$$
$$= \{x : p(x) \vee q(x)\}$$

and

$$P' = \{x : p(x)\}'$$
$$= \{x : \sim p(x)\}.$$

EXERCISES

1. Let $\mathcal{U}$ be the set $\{0, 1, 2, 3, 4, 5, 6, 7, 8, 9\}$. Let $A = \{1, 3, 5, 7\}$, let $B = \{2, 3, 4, 5, 6\}$, and let $C = \{0, 2, 4, 6, 8\}$. List the elements of each of the following sets. Use braces.

(a) $A \cap B$.

(b) $B \cup C$.

(c) $B \cap C'$.

(d) $A \cap (B \cup C)$.

(e) $(A \cap B) \cup (A \cap C)$.

(f) $(A \cap B) \cup C$.

(g) $A \cup \varnothing$.

(h) $B \cap \varnothing$.

(i) $A \cap C$.

(j) $\mathcal{U}'$.

2. Let $\mathcal{U}$ be the set of all positive integers from 1 to 10, inclusive. List the set of all elements in the complement of each of the following sets. Use braces.

(a) $\{x \in \mathcal{U}: x \text{ is even}\}$.

(b) $\{x \in \mathcal{U}: x \text{ is a square of a positive integer}\}$.

(c) $\{x \in \mathcal{U}: x \text{ is a one-digit number}\}$.

3. If $\mathcal{U}$ is the set of all points in a plane, what is the complement of the set of all points lying inside a given circle in that plane?

4. What is the complement of the empty set?

5. The universal set $\mathcal{U}$ of Figure 3.3 is divided into eight disjoint numbered portions. If A, B, and C are as in this figure, express each of the following as a union of numbered portions:

(a) $A \cap B$.

(b) $A \cap B'$.

(c) $A' \cap B'$.

(d) $(A \cap B)'$.

(e) $(A' \cup B')'$.

(f) $(A' \cap B')'$.

(g) $A \cap (B \cup C)'$.

(h) $(A \cap B) \cap C$.

(i) $A \cap (B \cup C)$.

(j) $(A \cap B) \cup (A \cap C)$.

(k) $A \cup (B \cap C)$.

(l) $(A \cup B) \cap (A \cup C)$.

(m) $(A \cap B)' \cap C$.

(n) $(A' \cap B') \cap C$.

(o) $(A \cap C') \cap (B \cup C)$.

6. Write an expression for each of the numbered portions of Figure 3.3 in terms of A, B, and C.

7. If the universal set $\mathcal{U}$ has just 17 elements and a subset A of $\mathcal{U}$ has just 5 elements, how many elements does A' have?

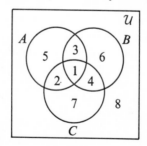

FIGURE 3.3

8. If the universal set $\mathcal{U}$ has a finite number of elements and A is a subset of $\mathcal{U}$, find a formula interconnecting $N(A)$, $N(A')$, and $N(\mathcal{U})$, if $N(A)$ is the number of elements in A, $N(A')$ is the number of elements in A', and $N(\mathcal{U})$ is the number of elements in $\mathcal{U}$.

♯9. Given finite sets A and B, let $N(A)$ be the number of elements in A, let $N(B)$ be the number of elements in B, and let $N(A \cup B)$ be the number of elements in $A \cup B$.

   (a) Find an expression for $N(A \cup B)$ if A and B are disjoint.

   (b) Find an expression for $N(A \cup B)$ if A and B are not necessarily disjoint.

   (c) Find an expression for $N[(A \cup B) \cup C]$ if A, B, and C are sets which are not necessarily disjoint.

   Hint: Draw a Venn diagram.

10. For military (combat) purposes human blood is classified as O, A, B, or AB, depending on which (or none, or both) of two antigens (called A and B) it contains. A safe transfusion is possible if and only if the recipient's blood has all the antigens of the donor's. A third antigen is important in human reproduction. Blood is said to be Rh-positive if it contains the Rh antigen, and Rh-negative otherwise. It is usually unwise for a woman with Rh-negative blood to receive Rh-positive blood.

   (a) Draw a Venn diagram classifying the set of all soldiers by blood type, indicating the sets of universal donors and universal recipients. [A universal recipient may safely receive anybody's blood; anybody may safely receive a universal donor's blood.]

   (b) Draw a Venn diagram classifying the set of all women by blood type, indicating the set of universal recipients.

   (c) Which type of blood would you guess to be in greatest demand? Why?

♯11. In a certain group of 100 hospital patients 45 had antigen A in their blood, 15 had B, 86 had Rh, 5 had A and B,

39 had A and Rh, 12 had B and Rh, and 4 had all three antigens. How many of these patients had blood which is of type A-positive? B-negative? O-negative?

#12. A certain fraternity reports that of its 100 members, 97 like blondes, 97 like brunettes, 98 like redheads, 94 like blondes and brunettes, 95 like blondes and redheads, 95 like brunettes and redheads, while 93 like all three kinds of girls. What is wrong with this fraternity?

#13. The 1956 *Combined Membership List* of the American Mathematical Society, the Mathematical Association of America, and the Society for Industrial and Applied Mathematics lists 9793 names. Of these, 5263 were members of the AMS, 6403 were members of the Association, and 1263 were members of the SIAM. Estimate to within 650 or so the number of people who were members of the AMS but not of the Association.

#14. In a certain city (unfortunately not Vancouver) all the men are devoted to wine, women, or song. Sixty per cent are devoted to wine, 75 per cent to women, and 70 per cent to song, while 45 per cent are devoted to wine and women, 40 per cent to wine and song, and 50 per cent to women and song. What is the percentage devoted to all three?

#15. Under what circumstances are the following statements true?

(a) $A \cup B = A \cap B$.
(b) $A \cap B' = A$.
(c) $A \subseteq \varnothing$.
(d) $A \cap B = B$.
(e) $(A \cup B) \cap B' = A$.
(f) $(A \cap B') \cup B = A \cup B$.

#16. Express the information contained in the statement "$P \subseteq Q$" in the form of an *equation* involving P, Q, and operations on sets. There are at least three solutions. *Hint:* Draw a Venn diagram.

*4. The Algebra of Sets

In the preceding section we noted that the operations, on sets, of intersection, union, and complementation correspond to the logical operations of **and, or,** and **not,** respectively. It is clear, furthermore, that this correspondence, or analogy, is very strong. Indeed, corresponding to the algebra of logic, studied in Part I, there exists an algebra of sets; and, moreover, this algebra of sets acts in essentially the same way as the algebra of logic. The basic laws, which hold for all subsets A, B, and C of a universal set $\mathcal{U}$, are the following.

1. (a) $\mathcal{U}' = \varnothing$.
   (b) $\varnothing' = \mathcal{U}$.

2. (a) $A \cap A' = \varnothing$.
   (b) $A \cup A' = \mathcal{U}$.   *Complement laws*
   (c) $(A')' = A$.

3. (a) $A \cap \mathcal{U} = A$.
   (b) $A \cap \varnothing = \varnothing$.
   (c) $A \cup \mathcal{U} = \mathcal{U}$.   *Identity laws*
   (d) $A \cup \varnothing = A$.

4. (a) $A \cap A = A$.   *Idempotent laws*
   (b) $A \cup A = A$.

5. (a) $A \cap B = B \cap A$.   *Commutative laws*
   (b) $A \cup B = B \cup A$.

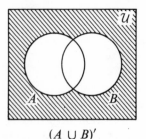

$(A \cup B)'$

FIGURE 4.1

6. (a) $(A \cap B)' = A' \cup B'$.
   (b) $(A \cup B)' = A' \cap B'$.   *De Morgan's rules*

7. (a) $(A \cap B) \cap C = A \cap (B \cap C)$.
   (b) $(A \cup B) \cup C = A \cup (B \cup C)$.   *Associative laws*

8. (a) $A \cap (B \cup C) = (A \cap B) \cup (A \cap C)$.
   (b) $A \cup (B \cap C) = (A \cup B) \cap (A \cup C)$.   *Distributive laws*

These laws can be verified pictorially by means of Venn diagrams or proved in a more detailed way by recourse to the truth table idea, together with the necessary definitions. Consider, for example, the De Morgan rule

$$(A \cup B)' = A' \cap B'.$$

This can be verified informally by means of the Venn diagrams of Figures 4.1 and 4.2. More detail can be found in the truth table

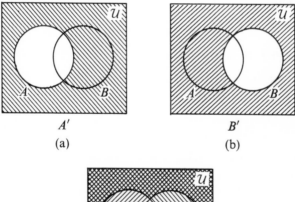

A'

(a)

B'

(b)

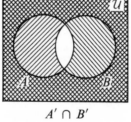

$A' \cap B'$

(c)

FIGURE 4.2

$x \in A$	$x \in B$	$x \in A \cup B$	$x \in (A \cup B)'$	$x \in A'$	$x \in B'$	$x \in A' \cap B'$
T	T	T	F	F	F	F
T	F	T	F	F	T	F
F	T	T	F	T	F	F
F	F	F	T	T	T	T
			↑			↑

FIGURE 4.3

of Figure 4.3. In this table, x is an arbitrary specific individual element of the universal set $\mathcal{U}$.

As already pointed out, the algebra of sets is quite similar to the algebra of logic. The only difference, really, lies in the notation. I trust that you will have little difficulty translating from one kind of notation to the other, and so I omit illustrative material.

EXERCISES

1. Use the algebra of sets to simplify each of the following:

   (a) $A \cap (A \cap B)$.
   (b) $A \cap (A' \cap B)$.
   (c) $(A' \cup B')'$.
   (d) $(A \cup B) \cap (A \cup B')$.
   (e) $A \cap [(A \cap B') \cup (A' \cap B)]$.
   (f) $[A \cap (A' \cup B)]' \cup B$.
   (g) $[(A \cap B') \cup (B \cap C')] \cap (A \cap C')$.
   ‡(h) $A \cap (A \cup B)$.

2. The *relative complement, $A - B$,* of a set B in a set A is defined as the set
   $$A - B = A \cap B'.$$

   Draw a Venn diagram to illustrate this operation.

3. Use the definition of the relative complement and the laws for the algebra of sets to prove the following:

(a) $A - (B \cap C) = (A - B) \cup (A - C)$.

(b) $A - (B \cup C) = (A - B) \cap (A - C)$.

♯(c) $(A - B) - C = (A - B) \cap (A - C)$.

♯(d) $(A \cap B) - C = (A - C) \cap (B - C)$.

(e) $(A \cup B) - C = (A - C) \cup (B - C)$.

♯(f) $A \cap (B - C) = (A \cap B) - (A \cap C)$.

(g) $A - (A - B) = A \cap B$.

♯(h) $A - (B - C) = (A - B) \cup (A \cap B \cap C)$.

(i) $(A - B) \cap (C - D) = (A \cap C) - (B \cup D)$.

4. *The symmetric difference, $A \triangle B$, of sets A and B is defined as the set*

$$A \triangle B = (A - B) \cup (B - A)$$
$$= (A \cap B') \cup (B \cap A').$$

Draw a Venn diagram to illustrate this operation.

5. Simplify each of the following:

(a) $A \triangle \varnothing$.   (c) $A \triangle \mathcal{U}$.

(b) $A \triangle A$.   (d) $A \triangle A'$.

6. Use the algebra of sets to prove that

$$A \triangle B = (A \cup B) - (A \cap B).$$

♯7. Express the union of A and B in terms of A, B, $\cap$, and $\triangle$. *Hint:* Draw a Venn diagram.

♯8. Use the definition of the symmetric difference and the laws of the algebra of sets to prove the following:

(a) $(A \triangle B) \triangle C = A \triangle (B \triangle C)$.   (*Associative law.*)

(b) $A \cap (B \triangle C) = (A \cap B) \triangle (A \cap C)$.

                                 (*Distributive law.*)

♯9. Construct an example to show that the equation

$$A \triangle (B \cap C) = (A \triangle B) \cap (A \triangle C)$$

does not always hold.

♯10. (By S. I. Birnbaum. Problem E 1203 in the *American Mathematical Monthly* (1956).)

(a) If $X = Y = \varnothing$, show that $(X \cap T') \cup (Y \cap T') \cup (X' \cap T \cap Y') = T$ for each subset T of $\mathcal{U}$.

(b) If $(X \cap T') \cup (Y \cap T') \cup (X' \cap T \cap Y') = T$ for each subset T of $\mathcal{U}$, show that $X = Y = \varnothing$.

5. *Quantifiers*

All and *some* are important words in mathematics. They make explicit the logical quantity of other words, and thus make communication more precise. Such expressions, involving the idea of "how many," are called *quantifiers*.

The aim of the present section is to relate quantifiers to sets and to logical operations. We begin with the so-called *universal quantifiers,* such as *all, for every,* and *for all.*

The standard example involving a universal quantifier is the proposition "All men are mortal." This proposition is a statement about the condition of being mortal—namely that all men satisfy this condition. Thus if M is the set of all men then the proposition "All men are mortal" states that the truth set, in M, of the open statement "x is mortal" is the entire set M. In general, *the statement that all elements of a set M satisfy a condition q means that the truth set Q of q, in M, is the entire set M.* In symbols,

$$Q = \{x \in M : q(x)\} = M.$$

This is often written as

$$(\forall x \in M)\ q(x).$$

[Read this as "For all x in M, $q(x)$."] When M is clearly known, this is often abbreviated to

$$(\forall x)\ q(x).$$

Example A. Let $\mathcal{N}$ be the set of all positive integers. Is it true, or is it false, that $(\forall x \in \mathcal{N})(x + 5 > 2)$?

Solution. The question is whether the truth set of the open statement "$x + 5 > 2$" is the entire set $\mathcal{N}$. Since the sum of a whole number with 5 is greater than 5, and consequently greater than 2, it is indeed true that $(\forall x \in \mathcal{N})(x + 5 > 2)$.

Example B. Translate the following statement in various ways: Every positive integer has the property that if you multiply the number following it by the number preceding it you obtain the number preceding its square.

Solution. For every positive integer x, $(x + 1)(x - 1) = x^2 - 1$. Or, in the set $\mathcal{N}$ of all positive integers the truth set of the equation "$(x + 1)(x - 1) = x^2 - 1$" is the entire set $\mathcal{N}$. Or, $(\forall x \in \mathcal{N})[(x + 1)(x - 1) = x^2 - 1]$.

In certain cases universal quantifiers can be related to the logical operation *and*. For example, to say that all men are mortal is to say that Nikita is mortal *and* Foster is mortal *and* Herman is mortal *and* Larry is mortal, and so on, to a listing of all men. Again, to say that $x + 5 > 2$ for every positive integer x is to say that $1 + 5 > 2$ *and* $2 + 5 > 2$ *and* $3 + 5 > 2$, and so on. Hence universal quantifiers express a general form of conjunction (*and*). For this reason the symbol "$\bigwedge$" is sometimes used instead of the symbol "$\forall$."†

The other quantifiers considered in this section are *existential quantifiers*. Examples of existential quantifiers are the expressions "there exists" and "some," used in the sense *there is at least one*. Consider the proposition "There is a tavern in the town." This proposition is a statement about the condition of being in the town—namely that the set of all taverns that satisfy this condition is not empty. If T is the set of all taverns then the proposition "There is a tavern in the town" states that the truth set, in T,

---

† Evidently, "$\bigwedge$" is better than "$\forall$"; but it is not as widely used.

of the open statement "x is in the town" is not the empty set. In general, *the statement that at least one element of a set M satisfies a condition q means that the truth set Q of q, in M, is not empty.* In symbols,

$$Q = \{x \in M : q(x)\} \neq \varnothing.$$

This is often written as

$$(\exists x \in M) \, q(x).$$

[Read this as "For some x in M, $q(x)$" or as "There exists an x in M such that $q(x)$."] As before, this is often abbreviated to

$$(\exists x) \, q(x)$$

when M is clearly known.

Example C. Is it true, or is it false, that $(\exists x \in \mathcal{N})(4x - 3 = x^2)$? [Here $\mathcal{N}$ is as in Example A.]

Solution. The truth set, in $\mathcal{N}$, of the equation "$4x - 3 = x^2$" can be shown to be $\{1, 3\}$. Since $\{1, 3\} \neq \varnothing$, the given statement is true. That is, $(\exists x \in \mathcal{N})(4x - 3 = x^2)$.

Example D. Is it true, or is it false, that $(\exists x \in \mathcal{N})(x + 5 = 3)$?

Solution. In $\mathcal{N}$ the truth set of the equation "$x + 5 = 3$" is empty. The given statement is therefore false. That is, $\sim (\exists x \in \mathcal{N})(x + 5 = 3)$.

In certain cases existential quantifiers can be related to the logical operation *or.* For example, to say that at least one man is crazy is to say that Nikita is crazy *or* Foster is crazy *or* Herman is crazy *or* Larry is crazy, and so on, to a listing of all men. Hence existential quantifiers express a general form of disjunction (*or*). For this reason the symbol "$\bigvee$" is sometimes used instead of the symbol "$\exists$."

EXERCISES

1. Let P be the set of all people. State in words the meaning of each of the following propositions:

   (a) $(\exists x \in P)(x \text{ loves Mary})$.
   (b) $(\forall x \in P)(x \text{ loves Mary})$.
   (c) $(\exists x \in P)(\text{Mary loves } x)$.

2. Let M be the set $\{1, 2, 3\}$. Determine the truth value of each of the following propositions, and defend your answer.

   (a) $(\forall x \in M)[(x + 1)^2 = x^2 + 1]$.
   (b) $(\exists x \in M)(x^2 + x = 6)$.
   (c) $(\exists y \in M)[\sim(y^2 + y = 6)]$.
   (d) $(\exists x \in M)(x^2 + 3x = 1)$.
   (e) $\sim[(\forall x \in M)(x^2 + x = 6)]$.
   (f) $(\forall z \in M)(z^2 + 3z \neq 1)$.
   (g) $\sim[(\exists x \in M)(x^2 + 3x = 1)]$.
   (h) $(\exists x \in M)(x^3 - x^2 - 10x = 8)$.
   (i) $(\forall x \in M)(x^3 - 6x^2 + 11x = 6)$.
   (j) $(\exists x \in M)(x^4 - 4x^3 - 7x^2 - 50x = 24)$.

3. Write each of the following as a statement involving a logical operation and the numbers 1 and 2.

   (a) $(\exists x \in \{1, 2\})(x + 2 = 3)$.
   (b) $(\forall x \in \{1, 2\})(x + 2 = 3)$.
   (c) $(\exists x \in \{1, 2\})(x^2 - 3x + 2 = 0)$.
   (d) $(\forall x \in \{1, 2\})(x^2 - 3x + 2 = 0)$.

4. State which quantifiers, what sets, and what conditions are involved in each of the following statements.

   (a) All differentiable functions are continuous,
   (b) All's well that ends well.
   (c) There are more things in heaven and earth, Horatio,
       Than are dreamt of in your philosophy.
   (d) All that glisters is not gold.

5. (a) Can a statement of the form $(\forall x \in \emptyset)\, p(x)$ ever be true? Explain.

   (b) Can a statement of the form $(\exists x \in \emptyset)\, p(x)$ ever be true? Explain.

6. De Morgan's Rules

We turn to the problem of finding negations of propositions containing quantifiers. We will treat the universal quantifier $\forall$ and let the reader discover how to handle the existential quantifier $\exists$ by himself.

We begin with an example. To negate the proposition "All men are mortal" we reason as follows: If it is false that *all* men are mortal then there must be at least one man who is not mortal, and conversely. Thus

$$\sim (\forall x \in M)\,(x \text{ is mortal}) \Leftrightarrow (\exists x \in M)[\sim (x \text{ is mortal})],$$

where M is the set of all men.

This example suggests that we may write

$$\sim (\forall x \in M)\, q(x) \Leftrightarrow (\exists x \in M)[\sim q(x)]$$

for any condition q. This result is correct; and it is easily derived from set-theoretic ideas as follows.

From the preceding section "$(\forall x \in M)\, q(x)$" means that the truth set Q of q is the entire set M. That is, $Q = M$. Therefore, "$\sim (\forall x \in M)\, q(x)$ must mean that $Q \neq M$. If Q' is the complement of Q in M this must mean that $Q' \neq \emptyset$. But from the preceding section this means that $(\exists x \in M)[\sim q(x)]$. Thus

$$\sim (\forall x \in M)\, q(x) \Leftrightarrow (\exists x \in M)[\sim q(x)]$$

as stated.

Note particularly that any proposition of the form $(\forall x \in M)\, q(x)$ is false if there is even one element x of M for which $q(x)$ is false. Such a disproving element is called a *counterexample* to the proposition.

Example A. How could one disprove the proposition "All men are fools"?

Solution. Find a counterexample! That is, find just one man who is not a fool. Although everyone else might be a fool—which would make the job of finding a counterexample difficult—the existence of this man would make it false to say that *all* men are fools.

Example B. If $\mathcal{N}$ is the set of all positive integers, find two counterexamples to the proposition "$(\forall x \in \mathcal{N})[(x + 1)^2 = x^2 + 1]$."

Solution. Since $(1 + 1)^2 \neq 1^2 + 1$ and $2 + 1 \neq 2^2 + 1$, two counterexamples are 1 and 2. [There are infinitely many more!]

The above law of negation is closely related to one of De Morgan's rules. This is the rule $\sim(p \wedge q) \Leftrightarrow \sim p \vee \sim q$ for propositions. For example,

$\sim$[All men are fools]
$$\Leftrightarrow \sim[(\text{Nikita is a fool}) \wedge (\text{Foster is a fool})$$
$$\wedge (\text{Herman is a fool})$$
$$\wedge (\text{Larry is a fool}) \wedge \cdots]$$
$$\Leftrightarrow [\sim(\text{Nikita is a fool}) \vee \sim(\text{Foster is a fool})$$
$$\vee \sim(\text{Herman is a fool})$$
$$\vee \sim(\text{Larry is a fool}) \wedge \cdots]$$
$$\Leftrightarrow (\exists x \in M)[\sim(x \text{ is a fool})].$$

Since the laws of negation for quantified propositions are so closely related to De Morgan's rules in logic, we shall refer to them as De Morgan's rules also.

EXERCISES

1. Let M be the set $\{1, 2, 3, 4, 5\}$. Find a counterexample to each of the following propositions:

    (a) $(\forall x)(x < 5)$

(b) $(\forall x)(x$ has just two whole-number divisors$)$.
(c) $(\forall x)(7 + 9x - 2x^2 < 17)$.
(d) $(\forall x)[(x - 1)^3 = x^3 - 1^3]$.
(e) $(\forall x)[\sqrt{(x - 2)^2} = x - 2]$.
(f) $(\forall x)(x^2 + 2 = 3x)$.
(g) $(\forall x)(x^4 - 11x^3 + 41x^2 - 61x + 30 = 0)$.
(h) $(\forall x)[(x + 1)^3 = x^3 + 3x^2 + 3x + 1]$.
(i) $(\forall x)(x < x^2)$.

2. Let M be a set, let q be a condition, and let Q be the truth set, in M, of q.

(a) Express the proposition

$$(\exists x \in M)\; q(x)$$

in set-theoretic terms.
(b) Formulate the negation of the result in (a) in terms of Q.
(c) Formulate the result of (b) in terms of Q'.
(d) Formulate the result of (c) as a proposition involving "$\sim q(x)$."
(e) State in words the way to find the negation of any statement involving one of the quantifiers $\forall$ and $\exists$.

3. Find the negation of each of the propositions of Exercise 2 of Section 5.

4. Given open statements $p(x)$ and $q(x)$ relative to a set M, find the negation of

(a) $(\forall x \in M)[\sim p(x)]$.
(b) $(\exists x \in M)[p(x) \wedge q(x)]$.

5. Express the negation of each proposition in Exercise 3 of Section 5 as a statement involving a logical operation and the numbers 1 and 2.

6. State the meaning of the word "proves" in the sentence "The exception proves the rule." Also, discuss the meaning of this sentence. *Hint:* See a good dictionary.

7. Multiple Quantification

In Part II we have made extensive use of open statements involving *single* unspecified terms such as "*x*." The purpose of the present section is to examine open statements involving *two or more* unspecified terms, and to see how they are affected by quantifiers.

To find out how to proceed we look back on open statements involving only one unspecified term. When such statements are combined with quantifiers, the results are *propositions*. For example, when the open statement "*x* is mortal" is combined with the universal quantifier ∀ (in the set *M* of all men) the result is the proposition "(∀*x* ∈ *M*)(*x* is mortal)." In English, "All men are mortal."

Now consider an open statement involving *two* unspecified terms—say "*x* is in love with *y*," and let us see what results when this statement is combined with a single quantifier. Suppose, for example, that *M* is the set {Charles, Roger}. Then "(∀*y* ∈ *M*) (*x* is in love with *y*)" is a statement that *x* is in love with both Charles and Roger. Since "*x*" is unspecified, this is an open statement expressing a condition—namely the condition of being in love with both Charles and Roger. Note that the new statement contains only *one* unspecified term, namely "*x*." The meaning of the "*y*" is completely determined by the quantifier ∀. If another quantifier, involving "*x*," is introduced then the result will be a proposition. In general, then, if a quantifier is combined with a statement involving unspecified terms, the number of unspecified terms in the resulting statement is diminished by one.

At this point it is advisable to allow different unspecified terms to refer to elements of different sets. If *M* = {Charles, Roger} and *W* = {Mary, Jane, Ruth}, then "(∃*x* ∈ *M*)[(∀*y* ∈ *W*)(*x* is in love with *y*)]" states that at least one of the men is in love with all three women. Similarly, "(∃*x* ∈ *W*)[(∃*y* ∈ *M*)(*x* is in love with *y*)]" states that at least one of the women is in love with at least one of the men.

Note that the *order* of quantification is important. The statement "$(\exists x \in W)[(\forall y \in M)(x$ is in love with $y)]$" is quite different from the statement "$(\forall y \in M)[(\exists x \in W)(x$ is in love with $y)]$." The first states that at least one of the women is in love with both men. On the other hand, the second states that a woman is in love with each man. The woman is not necessarily the same for both men. It is to emphasize the importance of order that square brackets were used in the above examples. These brackets will be dropped in what follows.

Many smooth-reading English sentences involve quantifiers in a form which may be hard to unravel. For example, consider the proposition "Any two similar triangles on the surface of a sphere are congruent." This is a compact way to express the following: Let T be the set of all triangles on the surface of a given sphere. Then $(\forall x \in T)(\forall y \in T)(x$ is congruent to y whenever x is similar to $y)$. [The result, by the way, is true.]

The last thing to be pointed out in this section is that the negation of statements involving several quantifiers is not much different from the negation of statements involving only one. This is illustrated in the following example.

Example A. Negate the proposition

$$(\exists x \in W)(\forall y \in M)(x \text{ is in love with } y).$$

Solution. Using the rules developed in the preceding section, we see that

$$\sim (\exists x \in W)(\forall y \in M)(x \text{ is in love with } y)$$
$$\Leftrightarrow (\forall x \in W)[\sim (\forall y \in M)(x \text{ is in love with } y)]$$
$$\Leftrightarrow (\forall x \in W)(\exists y \in M)[\sim (x \text{ is in love with } y)].$$

Thus to negate the statement that at least one woman is in love with all the men is to say that each woman is not in love with at least one man.

The work of Example A can easily be generalized to the following rule, with which we conclude this section: *To negate any proposition involving quantifiers, change every "$\forall$" to "$\exists$," every*

"∃" *to* "∀," *and negate the statement involving the quantified terms.*

EXERCISES

1. Let M be the set of all married men and let W be the set of all married women. State in words the meaning of each of the following propositions:

   (a) $(\forall x \in W)(\exists y \in M)(x$ is married to $y)$.
   (b) $(\exists x \in W)(\forall y \in M)(x$ is married to $y)$.

2. Let S be the set of all states of the U.S.A., let C be the set of all capitals of these states, and let $p(c, s)$ be the statement "c is the capital of s." Which of the following propositions are true?

   (a) $(\exists c \in C)(\exists s \in S)\, p(c, s)$.
   (b) $(\exists c \in C)(\forall s \in S)\, p(c, s)$.
   (c) $(\forall s \in S)(\exists c \in C)\, p(c, s)$.
   (d) $(\forall c \in C)(\exists s \in S)\, p(c, s)$.

3. Let $\mathcal{N}$ be the set of all positive integers. State which of the following propositions are true:

   (a) $(\exists x \in \mathcal{N})(\exists y \in \mathcal{N})(y = x + 7)$.
   (b) $(\forall x \in \mathcal{N})(\exists y \in \mathcal{N})(y = x + 7)$.
   (c) $(\exists x \in \mathcal{N})(\forall x \in \mathcal{N})(y = x + 7)$.
   (d) $(\forall y \in \mathcal{N})(\exists x \in \mathcal{N})(y = x + 7)$.
   (e) $(\exists x \in \mathcal{N})(\forall y \in \mathcal{N})(y + 1 < 3x)$.
   (f) $(\forall y \in \mathcal{N})(\exists x \in \mathcal{N})(y + 1 < 3x)$.
   (g) $(\exists y \in \mathcal{N})(\forall x \in \mathcal{N})(y + 1 < 3x)$.
   (h) $(\forall x \in \mathcal{N})(\exists y \in \mathcal{N})(y + 1 < 3x)$.

4. Give a reason why each of the false propositions of Exercise 3 is indeed false.

5. Let $\mathcal{R}$ be the set of all real numbers. State which of the following propositions are true:

   (a) $(\forall x \in \mathcal{R})(\forall y \in \mathcal{R})[(x + y)^2 = x^2 + y^2]$.
   (b) $(\exists x \in \mathcal{R})(\forall y \in \mathcal{R})[(x + y)^2 = x^2 + y^2]$.

(c) $(\forall x \in \mathcal{R})(\forall y \in \mathcal{R})[x(x+y) = x^2 + xy]$.

(d) $(\forall x \in \mathcal{R})(\forall y \in \mathcal{R})[(x < y) \lor (y < x)]$.

(e) $(\forall x \in \mathcal{R})(\forall y \in \mathcal{R})[(-x)(-y)$ is a positive number].

(f) $(\exists x \in \mathcal{R})(\forall y \in \mathcal{R})(xy = y)$.

(g) $(\forall x \in \mathcal{R})(\exists y \in \mathcal{R})(x + y + xy = 0)$.

6. Give a reason why each of the false propositions of Exercise 5 is indeed false.

8. *Equivalence of Conditions*

The foregoing work has indicated that there is a connection between conditions (or open statements) and sets. In a universal set $\mathcal{U}$ every condition yields a subset of $\mathcal{U}$, namely the set of all elements of $\mathcal{U}$ that satisfy the condition. The reverse is also true: Every subset of $\mathcal{U}$ yields a condition, namely the condition of being in that set. The set of all residents of Spain, for example, yields the condition of being a resident of Spain. As a result of this two-way connection between conditions and sets the study of conditions can be related to the study of sets, and vice versa. This connection is a valuable aid to the understanding of mathematics, and is worth further study.

First note that a condition completely determines its truth set. On the other hand, two different conditions can specify the same truth set. In the set of all triangles, for example, the condition of being equilateral (all sides of the triangle of the same size) defines the same set of triangles as the condition of being equiangular (all angles of the same size). Conditions like these, which specify the same truth set, are said to be *equivalent*. Of course, all this is relative to some universal set $\mathcal{U}$. Thus conditions p and q are equivalent to each other (in $\mathcal{U}$) when

$$\{x \in \mathcal{U} : p(x)\} = \{x \in \mathcal{U} : q(x)\}.$$

As an example of equivalent conditions defined by open statements consider the two statements "$x^2 - 4x + 4 = 0$" and "$x - 2 = 0$." These are different statements, but in the set $\mathcal{N}$ of all positive integers they specify the same truth set, namely $\{2\}$. Thus they are equivalent to each other.

As another example, consider the open statements "x is even" and "x^2 is even." These, too, are different statements. But in the set $\mathcal{N}$ they specify the same truth set, namely the set $\{2, 4, 6, 8, 10, \ldots\}$ of all multiples of 2. Thus, again, they are equivalent to each other.

Equivalent conditions (or open statements) are not equivalent propositions, but become equivalent propositions when applied to individual elements of the universal set $\mathcal{U}$. For example, if we apply the open statements "x is even" and "x^2 is even" to the specific number 6, we obtain the two equivalent (true) propositions "6 is even" and "6^2 is even"; again, if we apply these open statements to the specific number 3 we obtain the equivalent (false) propositions "3 is even" and "3^2 is even." [Recall that two *propositions* are equivalent if they are both true or both false.] Thus the present concept of equivalence is an extension of that given for propositions in Part I. Hence, we use the same symbol ($\Leftrightarrow$) for equivalence of conditions that we used for propositions.

To summarize, then, in a universal set $\mathcal{U}$ every condition p yields the subset $\{x \in \mathcal{U}: p(x)\}$ and every subset of A of $\mathcal{U}$ yields the condition of being in that subset, which may be expressed by the open statement "$x \in A$." These ideas are reciprocal in the sense that

$$A = \{x \in \mathcal{U}: x \in A\} \text{ and } p(x) \Leftrightarrow x \in \{x \in \mathcal{U}: p(x)\}.$$

Finally, *open statements $p(x)$ and $q(x)$ are equivalent to each other if, for all $x \in \mathcal{U}$, the propositions $p(x)$ and $q(x)$ are equivalent to each other.*

EXERCISES

1. Let $\mathcal{N}$ be the set of all positive integers. For each of the following pairs of equations $p(x)$ and $q(x)$, state whether or not $p(x) \Leftrightarrow q(x)$, relative to $\mathcal{N}$, and defend your answer.

$p(x)$	$q(x)$
(a) $x + 1 = 3.$	$2x + 1 = 5.$
(b) $2x + 3 = 9.$	$x(x + 1) = x^2 + x.$
(c) $x + 1 = 2.$	$x^2 + 3x + 2 = 0.$
(d) $x + 1 = 5.$	$x^2 + 2x = 24.$
(e) $(x - 1)(x + 2) = 0.$	$x^2 + x - 2 = 0.$
(f) $x - 1 = 7.$	$2x = 6.$
(g) $x + 1 = 0.$	$x^2 = 1.$
(h) $(x - 1)(x + 2) = 0.$	$x^2 - 2x + 1 = 0.$
(i) $(x^2 + 1)(x - 1) = 0.$	$x - 1 = 0.$
(j) $(x + 1)(x + 2) = 0.$	$(x + 3)(x + 4) = 0.$
(k) $\sqrt{(x - 1)} + \sqrt{(2x)} = 1.$	$x = 2.$

9. *Implication, I*

The relation of equivalence of conditions corresponds to that of equality of sets. Next we might ask what relation between conditions corresponds to the relation of inclusion between sets.

Let P and Q be subsets of a universal set U and suppose that P is a subset of Q. Then every element of P also belongs to Q. Expressed in another way, *if $x \in P$ then $x \in Q$*. [See Figure 9.1.] That is, the relation of inclusion between sets can be expressed as

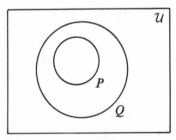

$P \subseteq Q$: *If $x \in P$ then $x \in Q$.*

FIGURE 9.1

an "if—, then—" relation between conditions. This relation is called the relation of *implication*. Formally, a condition p is said to *imply* a condition q if the truth set of p is a subset of the truth set of q. That is, p *implies* q if

$$\{x \in \mathcal{U}: p(x)\} \subseteq \{x \in \mathcal{U}: q(x)\}.$$

Of course, implication is relative to the given universal set $\mathcal{U}$.

Example A. In the set $\mathcal{N}$ of all positive integers show that the equation "$x + 1 = 3$" implies the equation "$(x - 2)(x - 3) = 0$."

Solution. The truth set of the first equation is the set $\{2\}$ and the truth set of the second is the set $\{2, 3\}$. Since $\{2\} \subseteq \{2, 3\}$, it follows that the first equation implies the second. Thus *if* a number satisfies the first equation *then* it must satisfy the second. This can also be reasoned through as follows: Suppose that y is a specific number in the truth set of the first equation. Then $y + 1 = 3$, so $y - 2 = 0$. Hence $(y - 2)(y - 3) = 0 \cdot (y - 3) = 0$. Therefore y must be in the truth set of the second equation also.

The above is a description of only one kind of implication— implication between open statements or between conditions. Other kinds of implication exist—for example, see the next section—but this definition does not apply to them.

Given conditions p and q, we shall write "$p \Rightarrow q$" or "$q \Leftarrow p$" to indicate that p implies q. These symbols may be read as

$$p \text{ implies } q$$

or as

$$\text{if } p, \text{ then } q$$

or as

$$p \text{ only if } q$$

or as

$$q \text{ is a necessary condition for } p$$

or as

$$p \text{ is a sufficient condition for } q.$$

All these expressions can be found in mathematical writings. Of course, the symbols "$p(x) \Rightarrow q(x)$" and "$q(x) \Leftarrow p(x)$" for open statements $p(x)$ and $q(x)$ can also be found, together with the attendant terminology.

Let P be the truth set of a condition p and let Q be the truth set of a condition q. Then $P = Q$ whenever $P \supseteq Q$ and $P \subseteq Q$, and conversely. Therefore $p \Leftrightarrow q$ whenever $p \Leftarrow q$ and $p \Rightarrow q$, and conversely. [Note how this is practically explained by the symbols $\Leftrightarrow$, $\Leftarrow$, and $\Rightarrow$ themselves.] Thus when a condition p is equivalent to a condition q it is often said that p is a *necessary and sufficient condition* for q. The phrase "*p if and only if q*" is also used to express the same idea.

If R is the truth set of a condition r then $P \subseteq R$ whenever $P \subseteq Q$ and $Q \subseteq R$. [See Figure 9.2.] Therefore, if $p \Rightarrow q$ and $q \Rightarrow r$ then $p \Rightarrow r$. [Here, again, this is practically explained by the symbol "$\Rightarrow$" itself.]

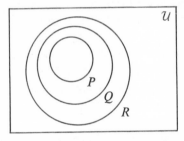

If $P \subseteq Q$ and $Q \subseteq R$ then $P \subseteq R$.

FIGURE 9.2

As an example of the foregoing, let f be the condition of residing in San Francisco and let c be the condition of residing in California. Since every resident of San Francisco is also a resident of California, it is clear that $f \Rightarrow c$. (Or, if a person resides in San Francisco then he resides in California. Or, he resides in San Francisco only if he resides in California. Or, residing in San Francisco is a sufficient condition for residing in California. Or, residing in California is a necessary condition for residing in San Francisco.) According to some information I picked up while touring the West Coast, to be truly happy one must reside in San

Francisco: All the truly happy people reside in San Francisco. Thus the condition h of being truly happy implies the condition f of residing in San Francisco. That is, $h \Rightarrow f$. Since $f \Rightarrow c$, it follows that $h \Rightarrow c$. Thus, to be truly happy one must reside in California.

A word about complements. Suppose that P and Q are subsets of a universal set $\mathcal{U}$ and P is a subset of Q. *Then Q' is a subset of P'.* This fact is illustrated in Figure 9.3. The analogue for conditions is as follows: If $p \Rightarrow q$ then $\sim q \Rightarrow \sim p$. Thus, if f and c are as in the preceding paragraph then $f \Rightarrow c$, whence $\sim c \Rightarrow \sim f$: If a person does not reside in California, then he does not reside in San Francisco.

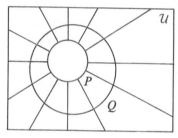

If $P \subseteq Q$ then $Q' \subseteq P'$.

FIGURE 9.3

EXERCISES

1. Let $\mathcal{N}$ be the set of all positive integers. For each of the pairs of equations $p(x)$ and $q(x)$ of Exercise 1 of the preceding section, state whether or not $p(x) \Rightarrow q(x)$, relative to $\mathcal{N}$, and defend your answer.

2. In each of the situations of Exercise 1 state whether or not $q(x) \Rightarrow p(x)$, and defend your answer.

3. A condition or open statement is said to be *universally true* in (or *relative to*) a universal set $\mathcal{U}$ if it is satisfied by every element of $\mathcal{U}$, and *universally false* in $\mathcal{U}$ if it is satisfied by no element of $\mathcal{U}$.

   (a) Which equations in Exercise 1 of the preceding section are universally true?

(b) Which equations in Exercise 1 of the preceding section are universally false?

(c) Show that a condition which is universally false implies every condition (relative to the universal set).

(d) Show that a condition which is universally true is implied by every condition (relative to the universal set).

4. Given the data of Exercise 2 of Section 2, prove: If x beat Boola, then x did not beat Boola by more than one touchdown.

5. Consider each of the following relative to the set U of all countries in North America.

(a) Show that the condition of having French as an official language is a sufficient condition for having English as an official language.

(b) Show that the condition of having English as an official language is not a sufficient condition for having French as an official language. [That is, show that the converse of (a) is false.]

(c) Is the condition of having English as an official language *necessary* for having French as an official language?

10. Implication, II

In the preceding section we investigated the relation of implication between conditions. We studied statements of the form "If—, then—" when they involved *conditions*. But statements of this form often involve *propositions* instead of conditions. Examples are readily constructed: "If taxes go down then I will be happy." "If $2 + 2 = 7$ then I'm a monkey's uncle." And so on. Since mathematics abounds in statements of this nature, the "if—, then—" form is worth close examination.

Any meaningful discussion involving propositions in general must ultimately be based on truth values, because truth values are the only things that all propositions have in common. From this it is clear that any general treatment of the implication "If p, then

q" must be based on the individual truth values of p and q. We shall find out how to proceed by examining the extreme forms of implication between open statements.

Let $\mathcal{U}$ be a universal set and let $p(x)$ be an arbitrary open statement relative to $\mathcal{U}$. Then $p(x) \Rightarrow x \in \mathcal{U}$, because the truth set of $p(x)$ is a subset of the truth set of "$x \in \mathcal{U}$," which is itself. An open statement, like "$x \in \mathcal{U}$," which is satisfied by all elements of $\mathcal{U}$ is said to be *universally true*. [Cf. Exercise 3, above.] Thus, relative to a given universal set, *any open statement implies an open statement which is universally true*. At the other extreme, open statements which are satisfied by *no* elements of $\mathcal{U}$ (such as "$x \in \varnothing$") are said to be *universally false*. Since the empty set $\varnothing$ is a subset of every set, this means that, relative to a universal set $\mathcal{U}$, *an open statement which is universally false implies any open statement*.

The above discussion suggests that a notion of implication applicable to all pairs of propositions should be of such a nature that any proposition implies a true proposition, and a false proposition implies any proposition. Thus we are led to say that a proposition p *implies* a proposition q if p is false or q is true. We shall write "$p \Rightarrow q$" to indicate that p implies q, and "$p \nRightarrow q$" to indicate that p does not imply q. Schematically, $T \Rightarrow T$, $F \Rightarrow T$, $F \Rightarrow F$, and $T \nRightarrow F$, where T and F are the truth values of the propositions under consideration.

At this point we have two kinds of implication, one for open statements (or conditions) and the other for propositions. They are related in the following way:

Suppose that $p(x)$ and $q(x)$ are open statements. If $p(x) \Rightarrow q(x)$, then, for each specific individual element y of the universal set $\mathcal{U}$, it turns out that the *proposition* $p(y)$ implies the *proposition* $q(y)$. On the other hand, if $p(y) \Rightarrow q(y)$ for each specific individual element y of $\mathcal{U}$, then it turns out that the *open statement* $p(x)$ implies the *open statement* $q(x)$.

A good way to understand the above relationship is to consider the truth sets P and Q of $p(x)$ and $q(x)$ respectively. If $p(x) \Rightarrow q(x)$ then $P \subseteq Q$. Hence, for a specific element y of $\mathcal{U}$, either $y \in P$ and $y \in Q$, or $y \in P$. [See Figure 9.1.] In the first case $p(y) \Rightarrow q(y)$, because $q(y)$ is true; and in the second case $p(y)$

$\Rightarrow q(y)$, because $p(y)$ is false. Hence, for *all* $y \in \mathcal{U}$, $p(y) \Rightarrow q(y)$. On the other hand, if $p(y) \Rightarrow q(y)$ for each $y \in \mathcal{U}$ then for each such y it is the case that $p(y)$ is false or $q(y)$ is true. That is, $y \notin P$ or $y \in Q$. The only way that this can happen for *each* y is for P to be a subset of Q. Hence $p(x) \Rightarrow q(x)$.

We know that each of two equivalent conditions must imply the other. It is easy to see that this result holds for propositions as well, for $F \Rightarrow F$ and $T \Rightarrow T$. Conversely, if each of two propositions implies the other then the propositions must be equivalent. Thus to say that $p \Leftrightarrow q$ is to say that $p \Rightarrow q$ and $q \Rightarrow p$.

The terminology used in connection with implication and equivalence between conditions will be adopted for use with propositions. Thus, if p implies q, we will say that p is a sufficient condition for q, and so on. This practice will simplify matters and cause no confusion.

Do not be disturbed by some of the silly conclusions allowed by the above definition of implication. For example, the proposition "$1 + 1 = 5$" does imply the proposition "Water is wet": If $1 + 1 = 5$ then water is wet ($F \Rightarrow T$). Such conclusions are harmless and do not affect the usefulness of the definition of implication.

Here are some more examples of implication between propositions:

Example A.   "$1 + 1 = 2$" $\Rightarrow$ "$2 + 2 = 4$" $(T \Rightarrow T)$.

Example B.   "$1 + 1 = 5$" $\Rightarrow$ "$2 + 1 = 17$" $(F \Rightarrow F)$.

Example C.   "$1 + 1 = 5$" $\Rightarrow$ "$2 + 2 = 4$" $(F \Rightarrow T)$.

Example D.   "$1 + 1 = 2$" $\nRightarrow$ "$2 + 1 = 17$" $(T \nRightarrow F)$.

Example E.   If p is *any* proposition (true *or* false) then

$$\sim\sim p \Rightarrow p.$$

This result can be obtained from a simple truth table.

Example F.   If p and q are *any* propositions then

$$p \wedge q \Rightarrow p.$$

This result can also be obtained from a truth table.

Example G.   If p and q are *any* propositions then

$$p \wedge q \Rightarrow p \vee q.$$

Examples E, F, and G are particularly interesting. The implication in these examples does not depend on the truth values of the component propositions, but only on symbolic form. This kind of implication is called *logical implication*. We can say that the *form* $p \wedge q$ implies the *form* $p \vee q$, or, alternatively, that if p and q are propositions then the proposition $p \wedge q$ *logically implies* the proposition $p \wedge q$. Correct reasoning is based on this idea of logical implication.

Example H. Decide whether the proposition "This is easy or I can do it. But this is easy," logically implies the proposition, "I can do it."

Solution. Let e be "This is easy" and let d be "I can do it." Then the problem is whether $(\sim e \vee d) \wedge e$ logically implies d. From a truth table it is not hard to see that $(\sim e \vee d) \wedge e$ must be false or d must be true. Therefore $(\sim e \vee d) \wedge e$ does logically imply d.

EXERCISES

1. Which of the following statements have a meaning equivalent to that of the statement "If you go I will go"?

   (a) I will go only if you go.
   (b) A necessary condition for me to go is that you go.
   (c) You will go only if I go.
   (d) A necessary condition for you to go is that I go.
   (e) A sufficient condition for me to go is that you go.
   (f) If you don't go then I won't go.
   (g) If I don't go then you won't go.

2. John and Dick, aged 13, are standing fully clothed on the dock. John promises Dick "I will jump in the water only if you do." Dick jumps in, and John stays on the dock. Has John broken his promise?

3. A lover promises "I will kill myself only if you refuse to marry me." She refuses to marry him. Is suicide the only honorable way out? Why?

4. A proposition of the form "If p, then q" has the same truth value as one of the form $\sim p \vee q$. From this, determine the truth value of each of the following:

   (a) I will eat my hat if $2 + 1 = 7$.
   (b) I will not eat my hat if $2 + 1 = 7$.
   (c) $2 + 1 = 7$ only if Paris is in France.
   (d) Paris is in France only if $2 + 1 = 7$.
   (e) $2 + 1 = 7$ only if I am Napoleon.

5. Which of the following *Therefore*'s represent examples of correct reasoning? [Note the information given in the preceding exercise.]

   (a) If it's WHIZ soap then it is good soap; it is good soap. Therefore it is WHIZ soap.
   (b) If I do not study I will sleep; if I am worried I will not sleep. Therefore if I am worried I will study.
   (c) We will invade Lower Slobbovia or a revolution will break out there; a revolution will not break out in Lower Slobbovia or the stock market will drop. Therefore if the stock market does not drop then we will invade Lower Slobbovia.
   (d) A necessary condition that we not invade Lower Slobbovia is that a revolution take place there; we will invade Lower Slobbovia. Therefore no revolution will take place in Lower Slobbovia.
   (e) He is not a good player or he is sick; for him not to be sick it is sufficient that he take care of himself; if he does

not take care of himself then he will be dropped from the team. Therefore if he is a good player then he will be dropped from the team.

11. Properties of Implication

As mentioned in the preceding section, correct reasoning is based on the idea of logical implication. The principal reason for this is the following rule, called the *rule of detachment:*

For arbitrary propositions p and q, if p *is true and if* $p \Rightarrow q$ *then* q *must be true also.*

Clearly, the rule of detachment expresses one of the chief features that correct reasoning ought to have. It allows us to *deduce* the truth of a proposition q knowing the truth of a proposition p and the fact that $p \Rightarrow q$. This rule is used over and over in mathematics and in other places where deductive reasoning is employed. Hence its importance.

The rule of detachment is easily proved: Merely note that $T \Rightarrow T$ and $T \not\Rightarrow F$. Thus if $p \Rightarrow q$ and $\tau(p) = T$, it is clear that $\tau(q) = T$ also.

There are other properties that implication should have, and does have. Here are a few, holding for all propositions $p, q,$ and r.

1. $p \Rightarrow p$. (*Tautology.*)
2. If $p \Rightarrow q$ and $q \Rightarrow r$ then $p \Rightarrow r$. (*Syllogism.*)
3. If q is false and $p \Rightarrow q$ then p is false also.
4. If p is true then $q \Rightarrow p \wedge q$.
5. (a) If $p \Rightarrow q$ then $\sim q \Rightarrow \sim p$.
   (b) If $\sim q \Rightarrow \sim p$ then $p \Rightarrow q$.
   (c) If $p \Rightarrow q$ then $\sim q \wedge p$ implies a false proposition f.
   (d) If $\sim q \wedge p$ implies a false proposition f then $p \Rightarrow q$.

The proofs of these properties are not hard. To prove property 2, for example, merely note that if $\tau(p) = F$ then $p \Rightarrow r$; and, if

$\tau(p) = T$ then it follows that $\tau(q) = T$, by the rule of detachment and the fact that $p \Rightarrow q$. Similarly, $\tau(r) = T$, whence $p \Rightarrow r$. Thus, whether p is true or false, if $p \Rightarrow q$ and $q \Rightarrow r$ then $p \Rightarrow r$.

EXERCISE

1. Do Exercise 5 of the preceding section in the light of the properties of implication covered in the text.

12. Indirect Proof

Some of the facts listed at the end of the preceding section are frequently involved in a useful technique called *indirect proof.* This is a technique by which one undertakes to prove that a proposition is true by tentatively assuming its negation. If this assumption leads to a contradiction, then the original assumption must be true.

Full understanding and appreciation of the force of indirect proof can come only through wide experience with this kind of proof. In the present book we must be content with very simple examples. Although very simple, the examples which follow do illustrate the basic principle involved. More sophisticated examples will come later in your mathematical career.

Example A. Suppose that we know that a particular positive integer x is greater than 6. Can we conclude that x is not the number 2? The answer, of course, is yes. What we do is note that 2 is not greater than 6, and therefore can not be the number x. This is an indirect proof. To prove that $x \neq 2$ we assume that $x = 2$ and deduce the contradiction $2 > 6$.

Example B. Mein Hut, der hat drei Ecken,
　　　　　　 Drei Ecken hat mein Hut;
　　　　　　 Und hat er nicht drei Ecken,
　　　　　　 So ist er nicht mein Hut. . . . (German song)

(My hat, it has three corners, three corners has my hat; and if it has not three corners, then it is not my hat.) This ditty is a concrete version of the fact that "$p \Rightarrow q$" and "$\sim q \Rightarrow \sim p$" mean essentially the same thing. Here p is "It is my hat" and q is "It has three corners."

Example C. John MacDonald is accused of having robbed a bank in Vancouver on September 13, 1957. His lawyer defends him in the following way: "I will prove that my client did not commit the crime (p: client committed crime). For if he committed the crime then he must have been in Vancouver at the time ($p \Rightarrow q$, where q: client was in Vancouver). Therefore he did not commit the crime if he was not in Vancouver at the time ($\sim q \Rightarrow \sim p$). Many incorruptible witnesses will testify that my client was in Ottawa when the crime was committed, not in Vancouver ($\sim q$). Therefore he did not commit the crime ($\sim p$)." If the lawyer can obtain the testimony of the witnesses (and hence prove that q is false) then his client has a perfect *alibi*. Note the missing hypothesis in the lawyer's argument: No person can be in Ottawa and Vancouver at the same time.

Example D. Suppose that x is a positive integer whose square x^2 is an odd number. We shall prove that x itself must be odd. Let p be "x^2 is odd" and let q be "x is odd." Assume, tentatively, that x is not odd ($\sim q$). Then x must be even, say $x = 2y$. Hence $x^2 = (2y)(2y) = 4y^2$ must be even ($\sim p$). This result contradicts the fact that x^2 is odd, thus proving that x can not be even, or that x must be odd. Alternatively, the argument shows that $\sim q \Rightarrow \sim p$. Hence $p \Rightarrow q$. Since p is true (that is, since x^2 is odd), q must then also be true (that is, x must be odd). We conclude with a warning. Although it happens to be true that $q \Rightarrow p$, this has no pertinence to our problem, which was to prove that $p \Rightarrow q$. The relation of implication is not symmetric, and must be treated with caution.

In sophisticated applications of indirect proof the proposition p in the statement "$(\sim q \wedge p) \Rightarrow f$" is a conjunction of a great number of propositions. The proposition f is usually of the form $r \wedge \sim r$, where r is a consequence of p or of $\sim q \wedge p$. Because of the complexity of p in these applications a symbolic rehash of the argument is usually not given.

*13. Problems by Lewis Carroll

Lewis Carroll, author of the celebrated *Alice's Adventures in Wonderland,* was in everyday life the Reverend Charles Lutwidge Dodgson, Mathematical Lecturer of Christ Church. In his *Symbolic Logic* he left problems which contain some of the madness that characterized *Alice.* Some of these are listed below. In each case the problem is to find the "best" conclusion, which is one using all the hypotheses. ("It will give you clearness of thought— the ability to *see your way* through a puzzle— · · · · *Try it.* That is all I ask of you!"—L.C.)

I.   (1) Babies are illogical;
      (2) Nobody is despised who can manage a crocodile;
      (3) Illogical persons are despised.

Univ. "persons"; a = able to manage a crocodile; b = babies; c = despised; d = logical.

II.   (1) Every one who is sane can do Logic;
      (2) No lunatics are fit to serve on a jury;
      (3) None of *your* sons can do Logic.

Univ. "persons"; a = able to do Logic; b = fit to serve on a jury; c = sane; d = your sons.

III.   (1) No ducks waltz;
      (2) No officers ever decline to waltz;
      (3) All my poultry are ducks.

Univ. "creatures"; a = ducks; b = my poultry; c = officers; d = willing to waltz.

IV.   (1)   No experienced person is incompetent;
           (2)   Jenkins is always blundering;
           (3)   No competent person is always blundering.

Univ. "persons"; a = always blundering; b = competent; c = experienced; d = Jenkins.

V.   (1)   No one takes in the *Times,* unless he is well-educated;
           (2)   No hedge-hogs can read;
           (3)   Those who cannot read are not well-educated.

Univ. "creatures"; a = able to read; b = hedge-hogs; c = taking in the *Times;* d = well-educated.

VI.   (1)   All the old articles in this cupboard are cracked;
           (2)   No jug in this cupboard is new;
           (3)   Nothing in this cupboard, that is cracked, will hold water.

Univ. "things in this cupboard"; a = able to hold water; b = cracked; c = jugs; d = old.

VII.   (1)   No name in this list is unsuitable for the hero of a romance;
           (2)   Names beginning with a vowel are always melodious;
           (3)   No name is suitable for the hero of a romance, if it begins with a consonant.

Univ. "names"; a = beginning with a vowel; b = in this list; c = melodious; d = suitable for the hero of a romance.

VIII.   (1)   All members of the House of Commons have perfect self-command;
           (2)   No M.P., who wears a coronet, should ride in a donkey-race;
           (3)   All members of the House of Lords wear coronets.

Univ. "M.P.'s"; a = belonging to the House of Commons; b = having perfect self-command; c = one who may ride in a donkey-race; d = wearing a coronet.

IX. (1) Nobody, who really appreciates Beethoven, fails to keep silence while the Moonlight Sonata is being played;

(2) Guinea-pigs are hopelessly ignorant of music;

(3) No one, who is hopelessly ignorant of music, ever keeps silence while the Moonlight Sonata is being played.

Univ. "creatures"; a = guinea-pigs; b = hopelessly ignorant of music; c = keeping silence while the Moonlight Sonata is being played; d = really appreciating Beethoven.

X. (1) Showy talkers think too much of themselves;

(2) No really well-informed people are bad company;

(3) People who think too much of themselves are not good company.

Univ. "persons"; a = good company; b = really well-informed; c = showy talkers; d = thinking too much of one's self.

XI. (1) No interesting poems are unpopular among people of real taste;

(2) No modern poetry is free from affectation;

(3) All *your* poems are on the subject of soap-bubbles;

(4) No affected poetry is popular among people of real taste;

(5) No ancient poem is on the subject of soap-bubbles.

Univ. "poems"; a = affected; b = ancient; c = interesting; d = on the subject of soap-bubbles; e = popular among people of real taste; h = written by you.

XII. (1) Promise-breakers are untrustworthy;

(2) Wine-drinkers are very communicative;

(3) A man who keeps his promises is honest;

(4) No teetotalers are pawnbrokers;

(5) One can always trust a very communicative person.

Univ. "persons"; a = honest; b = pawnbrokers; c = promise-breakers; d = trustworthy; e = very communicative; h = wine-drinkers.

XIII.   (1) No kitten, that loves fish, is unteachable;
          (2) No kitten without a tail will play with a gorilla;
          (3) Kittens with whiskers always love fish;
          (4) No teachable kitten has green eyes;
          (5) No kittens have tails unless they have whiskers.

Univ. "kittens"; a = green-eyed; b = loving fish; c = tailed; d = teachable; e = whiskered; h = willing to play with a gorilla.

XIV.   (1) There is no box of mine here that I dare open;
          (2) My writing-desk is made of rose-wood;
          (3) All my boxes are painted, except what are here;
          (4) There is no box of mine that I dare not open, unless it is full of live scorpions;
          (5) All my rose-wood boxes are unpainted.

Univ. "my boxes"; a = boxes that I dare open; b = full of live scorpions; c = here; d = made of rose-wood; e = painted; h = writing-desks.

XV.   (1) No one, who is going to a party, ever fails to brush his hair;
          (2) No one looks fascinating, if he is untidy;
          (3) Opium-eaters have no self-command;
          (4) Every one, who has brushed his hair, looks fascinating;
          (5) No one wears white kid gloves, unless he is going to a party;
          (6) A man is always untidy, if he has no self-command.

Univ. "persons"; a = going to a party; b = having brushed one's hair; c = having self-command; d = looking fascinating; e = opium-eaters; h = tidy; k = wearing white kid gloves.

XVI.   (1) No shark ever doubts that it is well fitted out;
          (2) A fish, that cannot dance a minuet, is contemptible;
          (3) No fish is quite certain that it is well fitted out, unless it has three rows of teeth;
          (4) All fishes, except sharks, are kind to children;

(5) No heavy fish can dance a minuet;

(6) A fish with three rows of teeth is not to be despised.

Univ. "fishes"; a = able to dance a minuet; b = certain that he is well fitted out; c = contemptible; d = having 3 rows of teeth; e = heavy; h = kind to children; k = sharks.

XVII.   (1) All the dated letters in this room are written on blue paper;

(2) None of them are in black ink, except those that are written in the third person;

(3) I have not filed any of them that I can read;

(4) None of them, that are written on one sheet, are undated;

(5) All of them, that are not crossed, are in black ink;

(6) All of them, written by Brown, begin with "Dear Sir";

(7) All of them, written on blue paper, are filed;

(8) None of them, written on more than one sheet, are crossed;

(9) None of them, that begin with "Dear Sir," are written in the third person.

Univ. "letters in this room"; a = beginning with "Dear Sir"; b = crossed; c = dated; d = filed; e = in black ink; h = in third person; k = letters that I can read; l = on blue paper; m = on one sheet; n = written by Brown.

Answers, Solutions, and Hints

SECTION 1-2

1. (c), (e), (k).

2. (d), (f), (l).

SECTION 1-3

1. *T*.

2. *F*.

3. (a) 4.
   (b) Any number different from 4 will do. For example:

   5, 6, 7, π.

4. *F*.

SECTION 1-4

1. (a) You are not beautiful.
   (b) The night is young or you are beautiful.
   (c) The night is not young or you are beautiful.
   (d) The night is young or you are not beautiful.
   (e) The night is not young and you are not beautiful.
   (f) The night is young.
   (g) The night is not young and you are beautiful; or the night is young and you are not beautiful.

2. (a) $\sim w$.   (c) $\sim j \vee a$.
   (b) $w \vee j$.   (d) $\sim w \wedge \sim j$.

(e) $\sim(w \wedge a)$.
(f) $(w \wedge a) \vee j$.
(g) $w \wedge (a \vee j)$.

(h) $\sim \sim a$.
(i) $\sim w \vee \sim a$.

3. (a) T.
   (b) T.
   (c) F.
   (d) F.
   (e) F.

   (f) T.
   (g) T.
   (h) F.
   (i) T.

SECTION I-5

1. The following answers contain only the last column of the truth table, made under the following conventions: In (a) through (e) column p reads TF; in (f) through (o) column p reads $TTFF$ and column q reads $TFTF$; and in (p) through (q) column p reads $TTTTFFFF$, column q reads $TTFFTTFF$, and column r reads $TFTFTFTF$.

   (a) TF.
   (b) TF.
   (c) TT.
   (d) FF.
   (e) $TTFT$.
   (f) $FFFT$.
   (g) $FFFT$.
   (h) $TFTT$.
   (i) $TFTT$.

   (j) $FTTT$.
   (k) $FTTF$.
   (l) $FTTF$.
   (m) $TFFT$.
   (n) $TTTT$.
   (o) $TTTT$.
   (p) $TTTTTFFF$.
   (q) $TTTTTFFF$.

2. (a) The last column of each reads $TFTT$.
   (b) The last column of each reads $TTTTTFFF$.
   (c) (a)–(b), (f)–(g), (k)–(l), (n)–(o).

4. 16, 32, 256.

5. $TTTTTFFFTFFFTFFF$, where p reads $TTTTTTTTFFFFFFFF$, q reads $TTTTFFFFTTTTFFFF$, etc.

SECTION I-6

1. (a) and (c), (a) and (d), (c) and (d).

2. The last column of each should read *FTTT*. [The conventions noted in the answers to Section 5 are followed here.]

3. (a) The night is not young, or you are not beautiful.
   (b) Joe is not slow and Jane is not plain.
   (c) Candy is not dandy, or liquor is not quicker.
   (d) The moon is not blue and my bonnie does not lie over the ocean.

4. The last column of each should read *TTTTTFFF*. [Conventions of Section 5.]

5. Patricia went to a play, or Queenie went to a ball and Ramona stayed home.

6. (a) Let $p = q = r =$ "$1 + 1 = 2$." [This, of course, is not the only solution.]
   (b) Let $p = q =$ "$1 + 1 = 5$" and let $r =$ "$1 + 1 = 2$." [Again, other solutions exist.]
   (c) No. This follows from any correct answer to (b).

7. Rod went to the races. This proposition is equivalent to the one given.

8. Jim went skiing. This proposition is equivalent to the one given.

9. If t is "triangle ABC is isosceles" and q is "quadrilateral $ABCD$ is a parallelogram" then the given proposition is $\sim[t \wedge (\sim t \vee q)] \vee q$, which is logically equivalent to "$1 + 1 = 2$." That is, it is *logically true*.

SECTION I-7

1. (a) *T*.
   (b) *F*.
   (c) *T*.

2. (a) T.
   (b) No solution.
   (c) T, F.
   (d) T.

3. Yes. [This is one of De Morgan's rules.]

4. (a) x.
   (b) $x \wedge y$.
   (c) F.
   (d) $x \vee \sim y$.
   (e) $x \wedge y$.
   (f) $\sim x \vee y$.
   (g) x.
   (h) T.
   (i) T.
   (j) x. In great detail:

   $$x \wedge (x \vee y) = (x \vee F) \wedge (x \vee y) = x \vee (F \wedge y)$$
   $$= x \vee F = x.$$

   (k) T. In great detail:

   $$\sim[(\sim x \vee y) \wedge (\sim y \vee z)] \vee (\sim x \vee z)$$

(1)	$= [\sim(\sim x \vee y) \vee \sim(\sim y \vee z)] \vee (\sim x \vee z)$
(2)	$= [(x \wedge \sim y) \vee (y \wedge \sim z)] \vee (\sim x \vee z)$
(3)	$= (x \wedge \sim y) \vee [(y \wedge \sim z) \vee (\sim x \vee z)]$
(4)	$= (x \wedge \sim y) \vee [\{(y \wedge \sim z) \vee \sim x\} \vee z]$
(5)	$= (x \wedge \sim y) \vee [\{\sim x \vee (y \wedge \sim z)\} \vee z]$
(6)	$= (x \wedge \sim y) \vee [\sim x \vee \{(y \wedge \sim z) \vee z\}]$
(7)	$= [(x \wedge \sim y) \vee \sim x] \vee [(y \wedge \sim z) \vee z]$
(8)	$= [\sim x \vee (x \wedge \sim y)] \vee [z \vee (y \wedge \sim z)]$
(9)	$= [(\sim x \vee x) \wedge (\sim x \vee \sim y)]$
	$\qquad \vee [(z \vee y) \wedge (z \vee \sim z)]$
(10)	$= [T \wedge (\sim x \vee \sim y)] \vee [(z \vee y) \wedge T]$
(11)	$= (\sim x \vee \sim y) \vee (z \vee y)$
(12)	$= (\sim x \vee \sim y) \vee (y \vee z)$

(13) $= \sim x \vee [\sim y \vee (y \vee z)]$
(14) $= \sim x \vee [(\sim y \vee y) \vee z]$
(15) $= \sim x \vee [T \vee z]$
(16) $= \sim x \vee T$
                     $= T.$

[The key steps are (1), (2), and (8). The others are more or less routine. Incidentally, this problem is related to the arrow operation of Exercise 5. And both problems become more intelligible when viewed in the light of Section 10 of Part II.]

5. (b) *F.*
   (c) *T.*
   (d) *T.*

6. The easy way is to form a "truth table" for "$x \rightarrow y$," using the results of Exercise 5. Harder, and more of a challenge, is to use the algebra of logic. Here are a few steps in (d):

$(x \rightarrow y) \rightarrow (\sim y \rightarrow \sim x)$
   $= (\sim x \vee y) \rightarrow (y \vee \sim x)$
   $= (x \wedge \sim y) \vee (y \vee \sim x)$
   $= [(x \vee y) \wedge (\sim y \vee y)] \vee \sim x$
   $= (x \vee y) \vee \sim x$
   $= T.$

7. (i) THEOREM. $[x \wedge (x \rightarrow y)] \rightarrow y = T.$
   (k) THEOREM. $[(x \rightarrow y) \wedge (y \rightarrow z)] \rightarrow (x \rightarrow z) = T.$
   [See, also, Section 11 of Part II.]

8. (a) *F.*   (c) *T.*
   (b) *T.*   (d) *F.*

9. The easy way is to form a "truth table" for "$x \veebar y$," using the results of Exercise 8. Harder, and more of a challenge, is to use the algebra of logic. Here are a few steps in (e):

$x \veebar y = (x \vee y) \wedge \sim (x \wedge y)$
   $= [x \wedge \sim (x \wedge y)] \vee [y \wedge \sim (x \wedge y)]$
   $= (x \wedge \sim y) \vee (y \wedge \sim x).$

The solution to (f) is more tricky:

$$x \vee (y \vee z)$$
$$= \{x \vee [y \vee z]\} \wedge \sim\{x \wedge [y \vee z]\}$$
$$= \{x \vee [(y \vee z) \wedge \sim(y \wedge z)]\}$$
$$\wedge \sim\{x \wedge [(y \wedge \sim z) \vee (\sim y \wedge z)]\}$$

[from the definition of "$y \vee z$" and from (e)]

$$= \{[x \vee (y \vee z)] \wedge [x \vee (\sim y \vee \sim z)]\}$$
$$\wedge \{\sim x \vee [(\sim y \vee \sim z) \wedge (y \wedge \sim z)]\}$$
$$= \{[x \vee (y \vee z)] \wedge [x \vee (\sim y \vee \sim z)]\}$$
$$\wedge \{[\sim x \vee (\sim y \vee z)] \wedge [\sim x \vee (y \vee \sim z)]\}.$$

And, by the same process, $(x \vee y) \vee z$ can be reduced to essentially this form.

Part (g) is tricky too:

$$x \wedge (y \vee z)$$
$$= x \wedge [(y \vee z) \wedge \sim(y \wedge z)]$$
$$= [x \wedge (y \vee z)] \wedge \sim(y \wedge z).$$

Also,

$$(x \wedge y) \vee (x \wedge z)$$
$$= [(x \wedge y) \vee (x \wedge z)] \wedge \sim[(x \wedge y) \wedge (x \wedge z)]$$
$$= [x \wedge (y \vee z)] \wedge \sim[x \wedge (y \wedge z)]$$
$$= [x \wedge (y \vee z)] \wedge [\sim x \vee \sim(y \wedge z)]$$
$$= \{[x \wedge (y \vee z)] \wedge \sim x\} \vee \{[x \wedge (y \vee z)] \vee \sim(y \wedge z)\}$$
$$= F \vee \{[x \wedge (y \vee z)] \vee \sim(y \wedge z)\}$$
$$= [x \wedge (y \vee z)] \vee \sim(y \wedge z)$$
$$= x \wedge (y \vee z).$$

10. $x = T, y = T, z = F$ or $x = T, y = F, z = T$.

11. "Or," in the sense "either—, or—, but not both."

SECTION I-8

2. The network of Figure 8.7 is
   (NOT X AND NOT Y) OR (X AND Y).

This is equivalent to
NOT (X OR Y) OR (X AND Y).

3. (a) Y (no black boxes needed).
   (b) X AND (Y OR Z).
   (c) X AND Y.
   (d) X OR NOT X = HOT.
   (e) X OR Y.
   (f) X OR NOT X = HOT.

SECTION I-9

1. $A = X \wedge \sim Y$.
   $B = \sim X \wedge Y$.
   $C = \sim X \wedge \sim Y$.
   $D = (X \wedge \sim Y) \vee (\sim X \wedge Y) \vee (\sim X \wedge \sim Y)$.
   $E = (X \wedge Y) \vee (\sim X \wedge Y) \vee (\sim X \wedge \sim Y)$.
   $F = (X \wedge Y) \vee (X \wedge \sim Y) \vee (\sim X \wedge \sim Y)$.
   $G = (X \wedge Y) \vee (X \wedge \sim Y) \vee (\sim X \wedge Y)$.

2. $X \wedge Y \wedge Z, \sim X \wedge Y \wedge Z, X \wedge \sim Y \wedge Z,$
   $X \wedge Y \wedge \sim Z, X \wedge \sim Y \wedge \sim Z, \sim X \wedge Y \wedge \sim Z,$
   $\sim X \wedge \sim Y \wedge Z, \sim X \wedge \sim Y \wedge \sim Z$.

3. $A = (X \wedge Y \wedge Z) \vee (\sim X \wedge Y \wedge Z)$.
   $B = (X \wedge \sim Y \wedge Z) \vee (\sim X \wedge Y \wedge \sim Z)$
   $\quad \vee (\sim X \wedge \sim Y \wedge \sim Z)$.
   $C = (X \wedge Y \wedge Z) \vee (X \wedge \sim Y \wedge \sim Z)$
   $\quad \vee (\sim X \wedge Y \wedge Z) \vee (\sim X \wedge \sim Y \wedge \sim Z)$.

4. Use a hall-light network! [See text.]

5. (a) *TFFFFFFF* or *FTTTTTTT* [Here we use the conventions made in the answers to Section 5.]
   (b) $X \wedge Y \wedge Z$ or complications.

6. (a) output$_X$: *FFFTTFFF*.
   output$_Y$: *FFTFFFTFF*.
   output$_Z$: *FTFFFFTF*.
   (b) output$_X = (X \wedge \sim Y \wedge \sim Z) \vee (\sim X \wedge Y \wedge Z)$.
   output$_Y = (X \wedge \sim Y \wedge Z) \vee (\sim X \wedge Y \wedge \sim Z)$.
   output$_Z = (\sim X \wedge \sim Y \wedge Z) \vee (X \wedge Y \wedge \sim Z)$.

7. X AND $Y =$ NOT (NOT X OR NOT Y).

8. (a) NOT $X = X$ STROKE X.
   (b) X AND $Y = (X$ STROKE $Y)$ STROKE $(X$ STROKE $Y)$.
   [Noting (a), make a diagram of this to see that only two STROKE boxes are needed, not three as a superficial examination of the solution might indicate.]

SECTION I-10

3. (a) $S_1' \vee S_2$.
   (b) $(S_1 \wedge S_2) \vee (S_1' \wedge S_2) \vee (S_1' \wedge S_2')$.
   (c) $(S_1 \wedge S_3) \vee (S_1 \wedge S_4)$.
   (d) $[(S_1' \wedge S_2) \vee S_3 \vee S_4] \wedge S_1$.

4. (a) $(S_1 \wedge S_2) \vee (S_1' \wedge S_2) \vee (S_1' \wedge S_2')$
   $= [(S_1 \vee S_1') \wedge S_2] \vee (S_1' \wedge S_2')$
   $= S_2 \vee (S_1' \wedge S_2')$
   $= (S_2 \vee S_1') \wedge (S_2 \vee S_2') = S_2 \vee S_1'$.
   (b) $[(S_1' \wedge S_2) \vee S_3 \vee S_4] \wedge S_1$
   $= (S_1' \wedge S_2 \wedge S_1) \vee (S_3 \wedge S_1) \vee (S_4 \wedge S_1)$
   $= (S_3 \wedge S_1) \vee (S_4 \wedge S_1)$.

5. $(S_1 \wedge S_2 \wedge S_3) \vee (S_1 \wedge S_2' \wedge S_3') \vee (S_1' \wedge S_2' \wedge S_3)$.

6. $(S_1 \wedge S_2 \wedge S_3) \vee (S_1 \wedge S_2 \wedge S_3') \vee (S_1 \wedge S_2' \wedge S_3)$
   $\vee (S_1' \wedge S_2 \wedge S_3)$.

SECTION II-1

1. (a) T.
   (b) F.
   (c) F.
   (d) F.
   (e) T.
   (f) F.
   (g) T.

2. Yes; yes.

3. $\{1, 2\}, \{1, 3\}, \{2, 3\}$. Three.

4. Ten.

7. Suitable universal set: The set of 17 people (or any set including this one). Six. [5 + 8 + 10 = 23, so 23 − 17 = 6 must take both.]

8. (a) {1, 3, 4, 5}.
   (b) {2, 11}.

9. (a) {1, 4, 5}.
   (b) {−1, 2, 3}.

10. (a) Being a nonzero digit.
    (b) Being a one-digit prime number. [A prime number is a positive integer with exactly two positive integer divisors —itself and 1.]
    (c) Being a primary color.
    (d) Being a color of the French flag.
    (e) Being an element of the set {the moon, 9, "*K*"}.

SECTION II-2

1. (a) {5}.
   (b) {2, 5}.
   (c) {2, 11}.
   (d) {5}.
   (e) {5}.
   (f) {1}.
   (g) {1, 2, 3, 4}.
   (h) ∅.
   (i) {1}.

2. (a) {Podunk, Riverford, State, York}.
   (b) {Ivy}.
   (c) {Podunk, State}.
   (d) ∅.
   (e) {York, Tech}.

3. (a) {California, Oregon}.
   (b) {Alaska, Washington}.
   (c) {California}.
   (d) {Alaska, Oregon, Washington}.
   (e) {Alaska, California, Washington}.
   (f) {California, Oregon, Washington}.
   (g) {Alaska}.
   (h) ∅.

4. (a) {Lake Erie, Lake Huron, Lake Ontario, Lake Superior}.
   (b) {Lake Michigan}.
   (c) {Lake Erie, Lake Ontario}.
   (d) {Lake Erie, Lake Huron, Lake Michigan, Lake Ontario, Lake Superior}.
   (e) ∅.
   (f) {Lake Erie, Lake Huron, Lake Michigan, Lake Superior}.

5. (a) {Buenos Aires, Mexico City, Rio de Janeiro}.
   (b) {New York, Chicago, Buenos Aires, Los Angeles, Philadelphia, Rio de Janeiro, Montreal, Boston, San Francisco}.
   (c) {New York, Chicago, Los Angeles, Philadelphia, Montreal, Boston, San Francisco}.
   (d) {Montreal}.
   (e) ∅.
   (f) {Sao Paulo, Rio de Janeiro}.
   (g) {Buenos Aires, Mexico City}.
   (h) {New York, Chicago, Buenos Aires, Philadelphia, Mexico City, Sao Paulo, Rio de Janeiro}.

6. Yes, one—itself.

7. (a) ∅, {1}—two.
   (b) ∅, {1}, {2}, {1, 2}—four.
   (c) ∅, {1}, {2}, {3}, {1, 2}, {1, 3}, {2, 3}, {1, 2, 3}—eight.

8. {1, 2, 3, 4}.

9. 16; 32; 64; $1024 = 2^{10}$.

10. Yes, but it was empty.

SECTION II-3

1. (a) {3, 5}.
   (b) {0, 2, 3, 4, 5, 6, 8}.
   (c) {3, 5}.
   (d) {3, 5}.
   (e) {3, 5}.
   (f) {0, 2, 3, 4, 5, 6, 8}.
   (g) {1 , 3, 5, 7}.
   (h) ∅.
   (i) ∅.
   (j) ∅.

2. (a) $\{1, 3, 5, 7, 9\}$.
   (b) $\{2, 3, 5, 6, 7, 8, 10\}$.
   (c) $\{10\}$.

3. The set of all points in $\mathcal{U}$ lying outside the circle or on its boundary.

4. The universal set under discussion.

5. (a) $1 \cup 3$.
   (b) $2 \cup 5$.
   (c) $7 \cup 8$.
   (d) $2 \cup 4 \cup 5 \cup 6 \cup 7 \cup 8$. [Strictly, only unions of *pairs* of sets have been defined, so this might be better expressed as $((((2 \cup 4) \cup 5) \cup 6) \cup 7) \cup 8$. However, by the associative law—see next section—it can be shown that the parentheses are not needed.]
   (e) $2 \cup 4 \cup 5 \cup 6 \cup 7 \cup 8$.
   (f) $1 \cup 2 \cup 3 \cup 4 \cup 5 \cup 6$.
   (g) 5.
   (h) 1.
   (i) $1 \cup 2 \cup 3$.
   (j) $1 \cup 2 \cup 3$.
   (k) $1 \cup 2 \cup 3 \cup 4 \cup 5$.
   (l) $1 \cup 2 \cup 3 \cup 4 \cup 5$.
   (m) $2 \cup 4 \cup 7$.
   (n) 7.
   (o) 3.

6. $1 = A \cap B \cap C$
   $2 = A \cap B' \cap C$
   $3 = A \cap B \cap C'$
   $4 = A' \cap B \cap C$
   $5 = A \cap B' \cap C'$
   $6 = A' \cap B \cap C'$
   $7 = A' \cap B' \cap C$
   $8 = A' \cap B' \cap C'$

7. 12.

8. $N(\mathcal{U}) = N(A) + N(A')$.

9. (a) $N(A) + N(B)$.
   (b) $N(A) + N(B) - N(A \cap B)$.
   (c) $N(A) + N(B) + N(C) - N(A \cap B) - N(A \cap C) - N(B \cap C) + N[(A \cap B) \cap C]$.

10. (a) Universal donors: Type O; universal recipients: Type AB.
    (b) Universal recipients: Type AB-positive.
    (c) Actually, O-negative is in greatest demand. It is the *only* type which O-negative women can safely receive. Even if it were abundant (which it is not) it would still be very useful because it can safely be given to anybody.

11. 35; 2; 6. *Hints:* First, make a Venn diagram and note that $35 = 39 - 4$. Write the numbers 35 and 4 in the appropriate places on the Venn diagram. Next, $N(B^+) = 12 - 4 = 8$; write the number 8 in the appropriate place. Next, $N(AB^-) = 5 - 4 = 1$; write the number 1 in the appropriate place. Next, $N(B^-) = 15 - 4 - 8 - 1 = 2$; write the number 2 in the appropriate place. Catch on? Now try for $N(A^-)$, $N(O^+)$, and, finally $N(O^-)$.

12. It issues inconsistent data. [The data imply that the fraternity has at least 101 members.] *Hint:* Make a Venn diagram and write the number 93 in the appropriate place. Now go on from there.

13. About 2750. Analysis: $N(A \cup S) \leq 9793$ and $N(A \cup S) \geq 9793 - 1263 = 8530$. Now $N(S \cap A') = N(A \cup S) - N(A)$. Hence $8530 - 6403 = 2127 \leq N(S \cap A')$
    $$\leq 9793 - 6403 = 3390.$$
    Evidently, 2750 approximates both 2127 and 3390 to within 650.

14. 30. *Hints:* Let x be the percentage devoted to all three. Then, for example, $45 - x$ is the percentage devoted to wine and women, but not song, $40 - x$ is the percentage devoted to

wine and song, but not women, and $60 - (45 - x) - (40 - x) - x = x - 25$ is the percentage devoted to wine, but neither women nor song. Continue in this way, finding appropriate percentages. Then note that the sum of certain percentages is 100. [It is a good idea to enter the various percentages on an appropriate Venn diagram.]

15. (a) When $A = B$.
    (b) When A and B are disjoint.
    (c) When $A = \varnothing$.
    (d) When $B \subseteq A$.
    (e) When A and B are disjoint.
    (f) Always.

16. $P \cup Q = Q; P \cap Q = P; P \cap Q' = \varnothing$.

SECTION II-4

1. (a) $A \cap B$.
   (b) $\varnothing$.
   (c) $A \cap B$.
   (d) A. *Hint:* $(A \cup B) \cap (A \cup B') = A \cup (B \cap B')$.
       [See Section I-2 if this gives trouble.]
   (e) $A \cap B'$. *Hint:*
       $A \cap [(A \cap B') \cup (A' \cap B)]$
       $= [A \cap (A \cap B')] \cup [A \cap (A' \cap B)]$.
   (f) $\mathcal{U}$. *Hint:* $A \cap (A' \cup B) = A \cap B$.
   (g) $A \cap C'$. *Hint:*
       $[(A \cap B') \cup (B \cap C')] \cap (A \cap C')$
       $= (A \cap B' \cap A \cap C') \cup (B \cap C' \cap A \cap C')$
       $= (A \cap C') \cap (B' \cup B)$.
   (h) A. *Hint:* $A \cap (A \cup B) = (A \cup \varnothing) \cap (A \cup B)$
       $= A \cup (\varnothing \cap B)$.

3. *Hints:*
   (a) $A - (B \cap C) = A \cap (B \cap C)'$
       $= A \cap (B' \cup C')$.
   (b) See (a).

(c) $(A - B) - C = (A \cap B') \cap C'$
$$= [(A \cap A) \cap B'] \cap C'$$
$$= (A \cap B') \cap (A \cap C').$$

[To discover this, work backward from $(A - B) \cap (A - C)$.]

(d) $(A \cap B) - C = (A \cap B) \cap C'$
$$= (A \cap B) \cap (C' \cap C').$$

(e) $(A \cup B) - C = (A \cup B) \cap C'$
$$= (A \cap C') \cup (B \cap C').$$

(f) $A \cap (B - C) = A \cap (B \cap C').$
Also, $(A \cap B) - (A \cap C)$
$$= (A \cap B) \cap (A' \cup C')$$
$$= [(A \cap B) \cap A'] \cup [(A \cap B) \cap C'].$$

(g) $A - (A - B) = A \cap (A \cap B')'$
$$= A \cap (A' \cup B).$$

(h) $A - (B - C) = A \cap (B \cap C')'$
$$= A \cap (B' \cup C).$$
$$= [A \cap (B' \cup C)] \cap (B' \cup B)$$
$$= A \cap [B' \cup (C \cap B)].$$

(i) $(A - B) \cap (C - D) = (A \cap B') \cap (C \cap D')$
$$= (A \cap C) \cap (B' \cap D').$$

5. (a) A.   (c) A'.
   (b) $\varnothing$.   (d) $\mathcal{U}$.

6. *Hint:* $(A \cap B') \cup (B \cap A')$
$$= [(A \cap B') \cup B] \cap [(A \cap B') \cup A']$$
$$= [A \cup B] \cap [B' \cup A'].$$

7. $A \cup B = (A \triangle B) \triangle (A \cap B)$.

8. See the answers to Exercises 9(f) and 9(g) in Section I–7, and note the resemblance between $\triangle$ and $\underline{\vee}$.

9. Try Venn diagrams. A particularly simple example is the one in which $A = \{1, 2\}$, $B = \{1\}$, and $C = \{2\}$.

10. (a) Direct: $X \cap T' = \varnothing = Y \cap T'$ and $X' \cap T \cap Y' = T$, etc.

(b) $T = X$ yields $Y \cap X' = X$, whence $\varnothing = Y \cap X' \cap X$
$= X \cap X = X$. Similarly, $Y = \varnothing$. Another solution:
$T = \varnothing$ yields $X \cup Y = \varnothing$, whence $X = Y = \varnothing$. [By
the algebra of sets,
$\varnothing = X \cup Y = X \cup Y \cup Y = \varnothing \cup Y = Y$, etc.]

SECTION II-5

1. (a) Somebody loves Mary.
   (b) Everybody loves Mary.
   (c) Mary loves somebody.

2. (a) F, because
   $$\{x \in M: (x+1)^2 = x^2 + 1\} = \varnothing \neq M.$$
   (b) T, because
   $$\{x \in M: x^2 + x = 6\} = \{2\} \neq \varnothing.$$
   (c) T, because
   $$\{y \in M: \sim(y^2 + y = 6)\} = \{1, 3\} \neq \varnothing.$$
   (d) F, because
   $$\{x \in M: x^2 + 3x = 1\} = \varnothing.$$
   (e) T, because
   $$\{x \in M: x^2 + x = 6\} = \{2\} \neq M.$$
   (f) T.
   (g) T.
   (h) F.
   (i) T.
   (j) F.

3. (a) $(1 + 2 = 3) \vee (2 + 2 = 3)$.
   (b) $(1 + 2 = 3) \wedge (2 + 2 = 3)$.
   (c) $(1^2 - 3 \times 1 + 2 = 0) \vee (2^2 - 3 \times 2 + 2 = 0)$.
   (d) $(1^2 - 3 \times 1 + 2 = 0) \wedge (2^2 - 3 \times 2 + 2 = 0)$.

4. (a) $(\forall x \in \mathcal{U})$ (x is continuous).
   $\mathcal{U}$ = set of all differentiable functions.

(b) $(\forall x \in \mathcal{U})(x$ ends well).
     $\mathcal{U} =$ set of all things that end well.

(c) $(\exists x \in \mathcal{U})(x$ is not dreamt of in your philosophy, Horatio).
     $\mathcal{U} =$ set of all things in heaven and earth.

(d) $\sim(\forall x \in \mathcal{U})(x$ is gold)
     $\mathcal{U} =$ set of all things that glister.

5. (a) Yes. *All* statements of this form are true, because
        $\{x \in \varnothing : p(x)\} = \varnothing$.

   (b) No, because $\{x \in \varnothing : p(x)\} = \varnothing$.

SECTION II-6

1. (a) 5.
   (b) 1 (or 4).
   (c) 2.
   (d) 2 (or 3 or 4 or 5).
   (e) 1.
   (f) 3 (or 4 or 5).
   (g) 4.
   (h) No counterexample exists; the proposition is true.
   (i) 1.

2. (a) $Q = \{x \in M : q(x)\} \neq \varnothing$.
   (b) $Q = \varnothing$.
   (c) $Q' = M$.
   (d) $(\forall x \in M)[\sim q(x)]$.
   (e) Change "$\forall$" to "$\exists$" (or "$\exists$" to "$\forall$") and negate the condition involved.

3. (a) $(\exists x \in M)[(x+1)^2 \neq x^2 + 1]$.
   (b) $(\exists x \in M)(x^2 + x \neq 6)$.
   (c) $(\forall y \in M)(y^2 + y = 6)$.
   (d) $(\exists x \in M)(x^2 + 3x \neq 1)$.
   (e) $(\forall x \in M)(x^2 + x = 6)$.
   (f) $(\exists z \in M)(z^2 + 3z = 1)$.
   (g) $(\forall x \in M)(x^2 + 3x = 1)$.
   (h) $(\forall x \in M)(x^3 - x^2 - 10x \neq 8)$.
   (i) $(\forall x \in M)(x^3 - 6x^2 + 11x \neq 6)$.
   (j) $(\forall x \in M)(x^4 - 4x^3 - 7x^2 - 50x \neq 24)$.

4. (a) $(\exists x \in M)\, p(x)$.

   (b) $(\forall x \in M)[\sim p(x) \lor \sim q(x)]$.

5. (a) $(1 + 2 \neq 3) \land (2 + 2 \neq 3)$.

   (b) $(1 + 2 \neq 3) \lor (2 + 2 \neq 3)$.

   (c) $(1^2 - 3 \times 1 + 2 \neq 0) \land (2^2 - 3 \times 2 + 2 \neq 0)$.

   (d) $(1^2 - 3 \times 1 + 2 \neq 0) \lor (2^2 - 3 \times 2 + 2 \neq 0)$.

6. Tests. The exception *tests* the rule.

SECTION II-7

1. (a) Every married woman has a husband.

   (b) There is a woman who is married to all married men.

2. (a), (c), (d).

3. (a), (b), (f), (g), (h). [In (g) let $y = 1$.]

4. (c) For each y, let $x = y + 1$, say.

   Then $y = x - 1 \neq x + 7$, so $(\forall y)(\exists x)(y \neq x + 7)$.
   This is the negation of the given proposition.

   (d) Counterexample: $y = 1$, say. [There are others.]

   (e) For each x let $y = 3x - 1$, say. Then $y + 1 = 3x \not< 3x$.

5. (b), (c), (f). [In (b) let $x = 0$; in (f) let $x = 1$.]

6. (a) Counterexample: $x = 1$, $y = 1$.

   (d) Counterexample: $x = 1$, $y = 1$.

   (e) Counterexample: $x = 1$, $y = -1$.

   (g) Counterexample: $x = -1$.

[There are other counterexamples to (a), (d), and (e).]

SECTION II-8

In each of the following, P is the truth set of $p(x)$ and Q is the truth set of $q(x)$.

1. (a) Yes; $\{2\} = P = Q$.

   (b) No; $\{3\} = P \neq Q = \mathcal{N}$.

   (c) No; $\{1\} = P \neq Q = \varnothing$.

(d) Yes; $\{4\} = P = Q$.

(e) Yes; $\{1\} = P = Q$.

(f) No; $\{8\} = P \neq Q = \{3\}$.

(g) No; $\varnothing = P \neq Q = \{1\}$.

(h) Yes; $\{1\} = P = Q$.

(i) Yes; $\{1\} = P = Q$.

(j) Yes; $\varnothing = P = Q$.

(k) No; $\varnothing = P \neq Q = \{2\}$.

SECTION II-9

In Exercises 1 and 2, P and Q are the truth sets of $p(x)$ and $q(x)$, respectively.

1. Yes for (a), (d), (e), (h), (i), (j), because $p(x) \Leftrightarrow q(x)$ Yes for (b), (g), (k), because $P \subset Q$. No for (c), (f), because $P \not\subset Q$. [See answers to Exercise 1 of the preceding section.]

2. Yes for (a), (d), (e), (h), (i), (j), because $p(x) \Leftrightarrow q(x)$. Yes for (c), because $Q \subset P$. No for (b), (f), (g), (k), because $Q \not\subset P$.

3. (a) $q(x)$ of (b).

   (b) $q(x)$ of (c), $p(x)$ of (g), $p(x)$ and $q(x)$ of (j), $p(x)$ of (k).

   (c) The empty set is a subset of every set.

   (d) Every subset of $\mathcal{U}$ is a subset of $\mathcal{U}$.

4. $\{\text{Ivy}\} = \{x \in F: x \text{ beat Boola}\}$
   $\subseteq \{x \in F: x \text{ did not beat Boola by more than one touchdown}\}$
   $= F$.

5. (a) The only North American country having French as an official language is Canada, where English is also official.

   (b) French is not an official language in, say, Bismarck, North Dakota.

   (c) Yes.

SECTION II-10

1. (c), (d), (e), (g).

2. No.

3. No; he said "only if," not "if."

4. (a) T.   (d) F.
   (b) T.   (e) T.
   (c) T.

5. (b), (c), (e). [This can be done by means of a truth table or by using properties of implication to be studied in the next section.]

SECTION II-13

I.   Babies cannot manage crocodiles.

     [(1) $b \subseteq d'$; (2) $a \subseteq c'$; (3) $d' \subseteq c$; so $b \subseteq d' \subseteq c \subseteq a'$.]

II.   None of *your* sons are fit to serve on a jury.

     [(1) $c \subseteq a$; (2) $c' \subseteq b'$; (3) $d \subseteq a'$; so $d \subseteq a' \subseteq c' \subseteq b'$.]

III. My poultry are not officers.

     [(1) $a \subseteq d'$; (2) $c \subseteq d$; (3) $b \subseteq a$; so $b \subseteq a \subseteq d' \subseteq c'$.]

IV. Jenkins is inexperienced.

     [(1) $c \subseteq b$; (2) $d \subseteq a$; (3) $b \subseteq a'$; so $d \subseteq a \subseteq b' \subseteq c'$.]

V.   No hedge-hog takes in the *Times*.

     [(1) $c \subseteq d$; (2) $b \subseteq a'$; (3) $a' \subseteq d'$; so $b \subseteq a' \subseteq d' \subseteq c'$.]

VI. No jug in this cupboard will hold water.

     [(1) $d \subseteq b$; (2) $c \subseteq d$; (3) $b \subseteq a'$; so $c \subseteq d \subseteq b \subseteq a'$.]

VII. No name in this list is unmelodious.

     [(1) $b \subseteq d$; (2) $a \subseteq c$; (3) $d \subseteq a$; so $b \subseteq d \subseteq a \subseteq c$.]

VIII.   No M.P. should ride in a donkey race, unless he has perfect self-command.

   [(1) $a \subseteq b$; (2) $d \subseteq c'$; (3) $a' \subseteq d$; so $b' \subseteq a' \subseteq d \subseteq c'$.]

IX.   Guinea-pigs never really appreciate Beethoven.

   [(1) $d \subseteq c$; (2) $a \subseteq b$; (3) $b \subseteq c'$; so $a \subseteq b \subseteq c' \subseteq d'$.]

X.   Showy talkers are not really well-informed.

   [(1) $c \subseteq d$; (2) $b \subseteq a$; (3) $d \subseteq a'$; so $c \subseteq d \subseteq a' \subseteq b'$.]

XI.   All *your* poems are uninteresting.

   [(1) $c \subseteq e$; (2) $b' \subseteq a$; (3) $h \subseteq d$; (4) $a \subseteq e'$; (5) $b \subseteq d'$; so $h \subseteq d \subseteq b' \subseteq a \subseteq e' \subseteq c'$.]

XII.   No pawnbroker is dishonest.

   [(1) $c \subseteq d'$; (2) $h \subseteq e$; (3) $c' \subseteq a$; (4) $h' \subseteq b'$; (5) $e \subseteq d$; so $b \subseteq h \subseteq e \subseteq d \subseteq c' \subseteq a$.]

XIII.   No kitten with green eyes will play with a gorilla.

   [(1) $b \subseteq d$; (2) $c' \subseteq h'$; (3) $e \subseteq b$; (4) $d \subseteq a'$; (5) $c \subseteq e$; so $a \subseteq d' \subseteq b' \subseteq e' \subseteq c' \subseteq h'$.]

XIV.   My writing-desk is full of live scorpions.

   [(1) $c \subseteq a'$; (2) $h \subseteq d$; (3) $e' \subseteq c$; (4) $a' \subseteq b$; (5) $d \subseteq e'$; so $h \subseteq d \subseteq e' \subseteq c \subseteq a' \subseteq b$.]

XV.   Opium eaters never wear white kid gloves.

   [(1) $a \subseteq b$; (2) $d \subseteq h$; (3) $e \subseteq c'$; (4) $b \subseteq d$; (5) $k \subseteq a$; (6) $h \subseteq c$; so $e \subseteq c' \subseteq h' \subseteq d' \subseteq b' \subseteq a' \subseteq k'$.]

XVI.   No heavy fish is unkind to children.

   [(1) $k \subseteq b$; (2) $a' \subseteq c$; (3) $b \subseteq d$; (4) $k' \subset h$; (5) $e \subseteq a'$; (6) $d \subseteq c'$; so $e \subseteq a' \subseteq c \subseteq d' \subseteq b' \subseteq k' \subseteq h$.]

XVII.   I cannot read any of Brown's letters.

   [(1) $c \subseteq l$; (2) $e \subseteq h$; (3) $d \subseteq k'$; (4) $m \subseteq c$; (5) $b' \subseteq e$; (6) $n \subseteq a$; (7) $l \subseteq d$; (8) $m' \subseteq b'$; (9) $a \subseteq h'$; so $n \subseteq a \subseteq h' \subseteq e' \subseteq b \subseteq m \subseteq c \subseteq l \subseteq d \subseteq k'$.]

Index